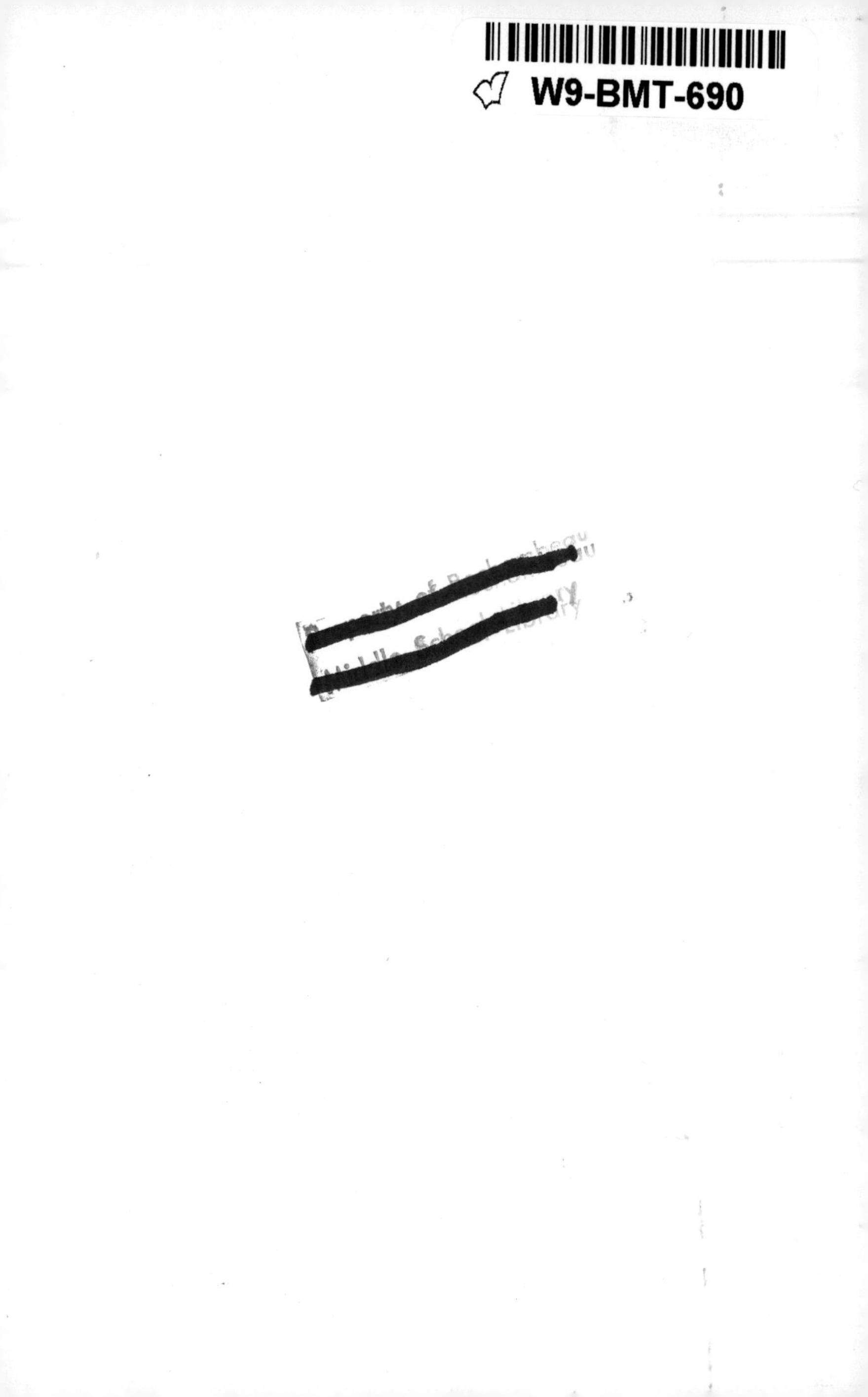

By Laura Hilgers

A *SPORTS ILLUSTRATED FOR KIDS* BOOK

Written by Laura Hilgers
Cover photograph © 1989 by Caryn Levy
Interior line art by Jane Davila
Produced by Angel Entertainment, Inc.

SPORTS ILLUSTRATED FOR KIDS Books is a joint imprint of Little, Brown and Company and Warner Juvenile Books.

Printed in the United States of America

First Printing: October 1990
10 9 8 7 6 5 4 3 2 1

Published simultaneously in Canada by Little, Brown & Company (Canada) Limited

ISBN 0-316-36239-5
Library of Congress Catalog Card Number: 90-050346

Contents

1
Going For the Shot

Nineteen-year-old Steffi Graf stepped up on the winner's stand in Seoul, South Korea, on an October day in 1988. She had just won the Olympic gold medal for tennis. As the West German flag was raised, an Olympic official placed the medal around Steffi's neck.

The medal was a fitting symbol for an almost perfect year. The finest athletes in each sport go to the Olympics—and Steffi was certainly the best woman tennis player in 1988.

That year, she did something that *no* tennis player—man or woman—had ever done before. The 19-year-old won a tennis Grand Slam *and* an Olympic gold medal! To win the Grand Slam, a player must win all of the four major tennis tournaments—the Australian Open, the French Open, Wimbledon (in Great Britain) and the U.S. Open—in the same year. Only four players (two men and two women) before Steffi had done so. An American named Don Budge won the first Slam in 1938. Before Steffi's, the most recent Slam was in 1970, when Margaret Court of Australia won it at the age of 28.

None of them, though, topped their Grand Slams with gold. They couldn't—tennis wasn't an Olympic medal sport between 1924 and 1988, and the Grand Slam wasn't recognized before the late 1920s.

Even if Steffi hadn't won the Grand Slam and the gold medal, she still would have made the tennis history books. In 1988, she lost only three out of 75 matches the entire year. From May 9 to November 18, she won 46 matches in a row!

Steffi had taken women's tennis to a new level—and there was no one there to join her. Her forehand was so powerful that reporters often called it "a weapon." And her feet were so fast that one tennis player said that she "had little wings on them." Most of all, though, Steffi had the steady concentration of a champion. She always wanted to win every point.

Despite her maturity on the court, Steffi was, in many ways, still a typical teenager off it. Although she is no longer a teenager, she's still a very down-to-earth girl. She likes to wear T-shirts, jeans and loafers—and she usually has stereo headphones on.

Steffi is very close to her family. When she isn't traveling around the world, she lives at home in Brühl [*Brool*], West Germany, with her father, Peter, her mother, Heidi, and her brother, Michael. Michael is two years younger than Steffi and he plays tennis, too. But he is not nearly as talented on the court as his sister.

For many years, the Grafs lived in the same home in which Steffi grew up, a one-story stone house off a busy street. It was right next to the tennis club that Steffi's father ran when she was younger. Even after Steffi had made millions of dollars, she and her family still lived in her modest childhood home.

In 1989, Steffi built another house for the Grafs. The new house is a triplex—it has three separate living quarters. One is for Steffi's parents. The other two are for Steffi and her brother.

Steffi doesn't have any desire to move away from her family. She plays in about 15 tournaments a year, and travels all over the world. She is traveling so often that for her, a vacation is when she gets to stay at home! "All the family is for Steffi," her dad says. "When we are all at home, it's the same as Christmas, or better than Christmas." When Steffi was once asked to name her fondest wish, she replied, "To live all the life long, but with my whole family, please."

She would probably want to live with her dogs, too. Steffi has three dogs—two German shepherds, Max and Zar, and a boxer named Ben. Steffi loves to play with her dogs whenever she is home.

Steffi looks to her family for strength. Her father, who is also her coach, almost always joins her on the road, so she isn't lonely. When Steffi's father can't travel, her mother goes with her. Her family is especially important to her because it is hard for her to maintain friendships. She doesn't have many tennis-player friends because she is always competing against them. And she can't spend much time with her friends in West Germany because she's not there that often.

For Steffi, the easiest part of being a tennis professional

is playing tennis. The hardest part is having to give interviews, sign autographs and attend official tennis functions. She gets paid to endorse several products, and she must make TV commercials or pose for printed advertisements for those products. She finds that all of those other parts of professional tennis are much more tiring than a three-hour match.

But Steffi can still relax and have fun on the road. She loves to play cards, read books and listen to music. In between matches, she will sit in a players' lounge and play cards with her father or her hitting partner, Pavel Slozil, who is paid to travel with the Grafs to keep Steffi's game in shape. Steffi's favorite card game is one called Doppel Kopf. "You can go crazy and get real mad at each other in this game," she says.

Steffi also likes to read. Her favorite authors are Ernest Hemingway and Stephen King. And she reads newspapers and magazines to stay informed on world events.

More than anything, though, Steffi likes to listen to music. "I am such a fan of music," she says. For a long time, her favorite musicians were Phil Collins and Bruce Springsteen. Now she likes more of a variety of music. When

Steffi arrives in a new city for a tournament, she always finds out if any exciting bands will be playing while she is there.

She has seen the British band Simply Red in Mannheim, only a few minutes from Brühl. She went to a Stevie Wonder concert in Ludwigshafen, also not far away. She saw George Michael in London, Tina Turner in New York, Noiseworks in Australia and Was (Not Was) in Paris. On a vacation in Marbella, Spain, she met Michael Jackson before one of his concerts. "Meeting these people is interesting because they are never as you expect after reading about them," Steffi told Curry Kirkpatrick, a writer for *Sports Illustrated.* "It's like my own stories. If I believed everything I read about myself, I wouldn't know me."

When Steffi is at home, she likes to listen to music in her room. Sometimes, she likes to turn down the lights, crank up the tunes and dance in the dark.

All the fun happens early because Steffi goes to bed every night at 9:00 P.M. Most kids complain when their parents make them go to bed so early, but Steffi wants to go to sleep then. She likes to get up early every morning, before the rest of the family. When she is home, she rides her bike to a bakery in Brühl to buy croissants and a newspaper and then goes home for a quiet breakfast alone.

The Grafs also have a home at the Polo Club in Boca Raton, Florida. Steffi likes staying in Florida because fans don't bother her as much as they do in West Germany. Some surveys have shown that Steffi is better known in West Germany than Chancellor Helmut Kohl, the head of the country's government.

Steffi's permanent home, though, will always be Brühl. She is loyal to her hometown. Germany has many charming and sophisticated cities and towns. Brühl is not one of them. It is a suburb of Mannheim, an industrial city in southern West Germany that natives compare to Buffalo, New York. It is not a glamorous city, which is perfect for Steffi because she does not care much about glamour.

"I think it's important we stick to our roots," says Steffi's dad. "Steffi is comfortable here. She can relax. It's important for her to appeal to the masses, important for the country that we stay."

Steffi's West German fans like her especially because she is just like one of them, even though she is a star. "Steffi, her father and the family may be boring, but it is vastly appealing that they are a normal, everyday German family coping with extraordinary circumstances," says a West German reporter. "They're doing a terrific job, I might add. We admire a loyalty to the country, closeness of family, the consistency this girl has shown on the court, the normality in her life."

West Germans are often described as being thrifty, disciplined and unemotional. By this definition, Steffi is very much a German. She earns millions of dollars a year, but the money doesn't mean that much to her. And she doesn't like to spend it. Once, when Steffi was in the airport in Frankfurt, West Germany, she saw a bag that she liked. When she saw that it cost $33, she put it down and said that it was too expensive. Then her mother bought it for her.

Another time, Steffi was in Chicago for a tournament, and the weather was much colder than she expected. She didn't have a coat. She called her father, who was not with her, and said, "Papa, it is snowing and I am freezing, but I have no coat." Her father told her to buy a coat. She said that the only one she liked cost $230. "Steffi," her father said, "you have millions of dollars. Go spend your money. Go get yourself a warm coat."

Steffi's discipline is legendary. She practices four

hours a day, and she is always trying to improve her game. Her father has to force her to take time off to relax. "I have to be careful with Steffi," he says. "Some people think I push her. That is not so. Steffi works much harder than the other girls because she wants to. That is why she is so good."

The press has compared Steffi to a German "machine" because she is so mechanical in her games and so unemotional in her victories. Steffi plays very quickly, never dawdling between points, and very efficiently. When she wins, she shakes her opponent's hand and then rapidly leaves the court. "I like to laugh," Steffi says, "but on the court it is my work. You do not laugh at work. I try to smile, but it is so difficult. I concentrate on the ball and not on my face."

The image of her as a machine is an unfair one, because Steffi really loves to play tennis. "My pleasure doesn't come from winning, but from the match itself," Steffi said a few years ago. "That great feeling is going for the shot—that's the most fun."

Having fun is what keeps Steffi playing. She is crazy about the game and always has been. She has had to make sacrifices to become the world's best woman player, but

Steffi couldn't be much happier. The reward is worth the sacrifice to her.

2

Crazy About Tennis

Stephanie Maria Graf was born on June 14, 1969. Her parents lived in Mannheim at the time. Steffi's father worked as an insurance salesman and a used-car dealer. In 1971, the Grafs had a son they named Michael.

Steffi's father was 27 years old when Steffi was born. He was the Number 1 player at his tennis club. He loved tennis, but he had started playing too late to make a career out of it. He decided to teach tennis to children at the club where he played. Steffi's mother was also a good tennis player, but she had to quit playing when Steffi was six because of a back injury.

When Steffi's parents were still able to play together,

they usually brought their children along to watch. Sometimes, Steffi's father would take her to the club when he was teaching. When they returned home, Steffi would bring one of her father's rackets to him and beg him to teach her. She said to him, "Oh, Papa, I want to play like you."

"She pestered me and pestered me," says her father. "I believed maybe she only wanted to play because she loved me and wanted to be like me." It's true that Steffi adored her father, but she also wanted to learn how to play tennis. Finally, her father took an old racket and sawed off a few inches so that Steffi could hold it. Steffi was only three years and nine months old.

After that, Steffi would greet her father at the end of every working day asking to play tennis. Steffi and her dad didn't play on a court. They played in the house, and only for a few minutes at a time. Steffi's dad stretched a string between two chairs in the living room and said the string was the "net." Then he showed Steffi how to hit the ball back and forth. She hit the tennis ball easily and naturally for someone so small. Her father would tell her, "If you hit the ball over the net 10 or 15 times, you get a Pepsi."

It wasn't long before Steffi was hitting the ball so hard

that she broke lamps. Steffi and her dad had to move their tennis games to the basement. There, they started using a couch as a net. Steffi quickly mastered the task of hitting the ball 10 times, and her father had to make the game more difficult. He promised her that if she returned the ball 25 times in a row, they would have a party. At their parties, they would eat ice cream with hot strawberries, and they'd listen to music.

Soon that became too easy for Steffi. Sometimes, on the 24th hit, her father would hit the ball so hard that Steffi couldn't return it. "You can't have parties all the time," he said.

During these games, Steffi's father noticed that his daughter concentrated completely on her playing. She always had her eyes on the ball just as she does today. Nothing distracted her, which is unusual in a very young child. Even if the telephone rang, Steffi did not look away.

When Steffi was five, she graduated from the basement to a real tennis court. The large court didn't scare her, and she continued to play with her father. But she also started playing against kids her own age and some even older. Steffi liked to play the eight-year-olds at her father's tennis club.

They probably thought that Steffi would be a pushover — before they played her. She beat them all!

Steffi won her first tennis tournament when she was six. The tournament was a juniors event held in Munich, West Germany.

Steffi was crazy about tennis. She couldn't wait to get out of *Grundschule* ([*GROOND-shoo-lah*] means grade school) and get onto the court. Some parents pressure their children to work hard at sports, but Steffi's parents didn't have to. She always wanted to play more than her parents thought she should. "I saw so many players whose parents put pressure on them. They would say, 'You have to play tennis today,'" says Steffi's father. "With Steffi, you never had to say that. With her, I would say, 'Okay, I think we can play today,' and then she was always at the court earlier than the time we were scheduled to play."

Steffi was very serious about tennis even when she was young. Once, she was invited to a schoolmate's birthday party to be held after school, but Steffi told her friend she couldn't make it because she had to practice. "I made her go to the party," says Steffi's father. Steffi was willing to give up playing with friends after school in order to play tennis.

"Steffi has always been crazy about tennis. And that's all," says Claudia Kohde-Kilsch [*CODE-a-killsh*], a West German tennis player who's friendly with Steffi.

Steffi took tennis lessons at her parents' club and also with the German Tennis Federation program in Liemen [*LYE-men*], about six miles away from her house. In Liemen, seven-year-old Steffi met nine-year-old Boris Becker. Boris lived just a few minutes' walk away from the club were they played tennis. Boris and Steffi practiced together often. "I was the worst in the boys," Boris recalls. "She was the best in the girls—so I had to hit with her."

She and Boris have been keeping track of each other for years, through the junior events and into the big time. "We more or less went through the same tournaments and kept a relationship," says Boris.

When Steffi was seven, her father decided that he should be her only coach. He thought that federation coaches didn't understand Steffi's game as well as he did. He could see that she had tremendous ability, and he could already tell that his daughter would one day be good enough to become a tennis pro.

Steffi's father sold his insurance and car businesses,

and moved the family to Brühl when she was eight. He built the Graf Tennis Club, with three outdoor and three indoor courts, right next to their house. He began coaching Steffi for an hour or two every day after school.

Steffi's father is still her coach. Some kids might think this would be hard on both of them, but Steffi doesn't. "It is very good to have my father as my coach," she says. "He knows me best." When she disagrees with him, she tells him. Both Steffi and her father are very stubborn, and sometimes they fight. But most of the time, they have fun together. "It has never been difficult to coach Steffi," says her father. "We have a very good relationship. She's very disciplined. I never have to tell her to work."

As Steffi's game progressed, her father traveled with her to almost every tournament, watched just about every match and advised her on how to approach a particular opponent. Steffi's mother and brother went to a lot of her matches, too.

Steffi's father has also had to fight some battles for her. He protected Steffi from the press, from money-hungry agents and from the hordes of fans. Mr. Graf has argued with tennis officials when he thought that Steffi was treated unfairly. He may have made an enemy or two along the way, but he was only looking out for his daughter's best interests.

"Papa never pressures me to win," Steffi said. "If I win, I win; if I lose, I lose. It helps me so much to stay calm. People don't understand Papa. The things he does are to take pressure off, not to make it worse. He tries to keep all the bad things away and protect me."

Neither Steffi nor her dad expected that she would become so good so quickly. "It all happened very naturally. It seemed like I was playing in tournaments and always moving up to the next level without thinking about it. I was just thinking about having a good time," says Steffi.

Steffi won her age-group championship in West Germany when she was eight years old. Isabel Cueto [*QUAY-to*], a German tennis player, saw Steffi play that year. Isabel told *Sports Illustrated*, "I saw Steffi in a tournament when she was eight. Her forehand wasn't even her best shot then. She had such a beautiful backhand. No slice or topspin, no nothing. I was nine. My parents and I couldn't believe it. They knew I would need some more lessons."

Every year after that, Steffi became the champion of her age group. In 1981, when she was 12 years old, Steffi won the German 14-and-unders, and she also won the 18-and-unders.

The next year, while she was still 12, Steffi won the European 12-and-under championships, playing against girls from all over Eastern Europe. Steffi was already so good that she was ranked 12th among all West German *adults*! Steffi turned pro in the fall of 1982, when she was only 13 years and 4 months old. The Women's International Tennis Association ranked her 214th in the world.

Becoming a professional tennis player meant that Steffi had to quit school. She was an eighth-grader at a *Realschule* [*ray-AL-shoo-lah*] in Brühl. A *Realschule* is a six-year school, for students from fifth to tenth grade. So Steffi's father hired a tutor to travel with her to tournaments for a couple of years after she turned pro. Steffi worked with her tutor until she was 15, and then she continued her studies by mail. Along with her rackets and tennis shoes, she carried sociology, government and physics schoolbooks to tournaments. She admitted, though, that "physics is the book I like least to put in my hand."

To this day, Steffi has not earned the equivalent of a high school degree in the United States. Most likely, she will never go to college.

Still, Steffi is an intelligent young woman, and she has received an education that four years of college could never match. She speaks English and French, as well as her native German. Steffi has been almost everywhere in the world and seen most of the world's major cities.

When Steffi first joined the women's tour, she felt lucky to get past the first round of a tournament, especially if it was a major event. But in 1983, she made it to the quarterfinals of a tournament in Warwickshire, England, and the semifinals of an event in Freiburg, West Germany.

Steffi had less luck in Grand Slam events. In Paris in May 1983, 13-year-old Steffi made it to the second round of the French Open—and then lost.

At the Australian Open, in December 1983, Steffi didn't even make it through the first round. She fell on the grass courts of Kooyong Club in Melbourne, Australia, during a practice session. She stopped her fall with her hand and tore the tendons in her thumb. Despite the pain, Steffi played the first set of the match, losing 6-1. After that set, she withdrew from the tournament, very disappointed.

Martina Navratilova [*na-VRAH-tah-lo-va*] was then

the Number 1 woman tennis player in the world. She had heard of Steffi's misfortune, and sent her a note. Martina's message was simple: *Take your time. Stay in school. Don't rush your career*. The 14-year-old Steffi was thrilled that Martina had written to her. And when Steffi took the Number 1 spot away from Martina in 1987, Martina probably wished that Steffi *had* stayed in school!

Not all the top players were as nice as Martina. In October of 1983, when Steffi was 13, she played an exhibition match against Tracy Austin of the U.S.A. in Filderstadt [*FEEL-der-stat*], West Germany. Tracy was 20 years old and one of the top players in the world at the time, but she was beginning to slow down because of recurring neck and back injuries. Steffi was still small then (about 5'3"), but she packed enormous power into her groundstrokes—her forehand and backhand. She took Austin to 4-all in the first set. After that, though, Tracy won eight games in a row, and won the match 6-4, 6-0.

After the match was over, West German reporters surrounded Tracy. "What do you think of our Steffi?" they asked the American player. "Does she have a chance to be Number 1 someday?"

"There are a hundred like her back in the States," Tracy replied.

Steffi's father couldn't believe that Tracy could be so rude. "I never forget this remark," he said. Tracy probably won't forget it either.

There aren't a hundred—there isn't even *one*—like Steffi in the whole *world.*

3
A Rising Star

As Steffi grew stronger, she began to win more often and gain confidence. But she still wasn't making her way to the final rounds in the tournaments.

In 1984, when Steffi was 15, she made it to the quarter-finals of the German Open, and the finals of the tournament at Filderstadt, West Germany. But in the Grand Slam events, Steffi was happy to just get beyond the first round, which she did at both the French Open and Wimbledon that year.

In May, Steffi played in the third round of the French Open. She lost that round to her German friend, Claudia Kohde-Kilsch.

Then Steffi got to the fourth round of Wimbledon. A

fourth-round exit may not sound so great, but Steffi was happy. She was still very young, and Wimbledon was the most prestigious of all the Grand Slam tournaments.

Why is it so prestigious? The tournament is held at one of the oldest tennis clubs in the world, the All England Lawn Tennis and Croquet Club, which is located in a London suburb called Wimbledon. The club, and the tournament, are rich in tennis tradition.

The Club was built in 1868 as a croquet club. In 1875, only two years after tennis was invented, grass tennis courts were added. In 1877, the first tennis championships were held at Wimbledon.

The Club now has 18 grass courts, all of which must be mowed daily. There are also 3,000 flowering plants scattered around the courts. It takes 26 groundskeepers to mow the grass and water all of the plants.

Wimbledon's Centre Court, where the most important matches are played, is called "the Cathedral of Tennis." Tennis is treated almost like a religion at the club. Centre Court has a Royal Box, where tennis fans in the royal family, like Princess Diana of England and her sister-in-law, Sarah, the Duchess of York (also known as "Fergie"), sit to watch matches. Queen Elizabeth makes an occasional appearance as well. She attended the tournament in 1962, 1975 and 1977, which was the 100th anniversary of the tournament.

The players themselves are often treated like royalty at the tournament. They ride from their hotels in London to Wimbledon in chauffeured cars, and at the club there is a tearoom for players. It is a British tradition to have tea, with sandwiches and cakes, in the afternoon.

Players must also obey specific rules: They must dress in predominantly white tennis clothes; all linesmen and lineswomen must wear green jackets; the winner and loser must walk off together at the end of a match on Centre Court.

Steffi didn't have to worry about Centre Court in 1984. Her fourth-round loss to British player Jo Durie took place on an outer court. It wasn't long, though, before Steffi found her way to a winner's court.

A month after Wimbledon, Steffi flew to Los Angeles to play in the 1984 Olympics. Tennis was just a demonstration sport, and the competition was only open to players aged 21 and under.

Thirty-two players came from 22 countries to compete. At 15 years and two months, Steffi was the youngest player in the tournament. She played like an older champion, though, mowing down every opponent she faced at the University of California Tennis Center. In the final, she defeated Sabrina Goles of Yugoslavia. Steffi had won her first international tournament—and an honorary gold medal!

Steffi and Stefan Edberg, the young Swede who won the men's gold medal, were delighted. Stefan has since gone on to a very successful tennis career, like Steffi. The gold was obviously a hint of greater things to come for both of them.

Steffi enjoyed being in Los Angeles. She was excited to be around the greatest athletes in the world. She loved southern California. Steffi liked running on the beach with her brother. She was a very good runner, and the beach was peaceful. Steffi wasn't a star yet, so she could run without being recognized and stopped by fans who wanted her autograph. Los Angeles is obviously very different from the industrial environment of Brühl.

In 1985, Steffi began to make her mark in tennis. She started the year ranked 22nd in the world, and she had grown to 5"8" and 111 pounds, only slightly smaller than she is today. More than anything, Steffi wanted to make it into the Top 10.

Steffi made it to the semifinals of the Lipton International Players Championships held in Boca Raton, Florida, in February. There, she faced a woman she had admired for years—Chris Evert.

Steffi had once said, "I would like to attack as well as Martina [Navratilova] and defend as well as Chris." Martina was an "attacker" because she always served very hard, and then rushed to the net to volley. Her style is called "serve-and-volley." Chris, on the other hand, was a "defender" because she stayed close to the baseline (the line that marks the back of the court), hitting wonderful groundstrokes and waiting for her opponent to make mistakes.

Chris's strategy worked well against Steffi. She beat the young West German, 6-4, 6-2. But Chris saw how masterfully Steffi played, and she guessed that Steffi might be a future star. Only a year after their meeting, Chris said, "Steffi is determined, tough to beat and has the right mental attitude. I've said all along that Steffi definitely has the game to contend for Number 1."

Steffi made it to the finals of the German Open as well

as the Fort Lauderdale and Mahwah, New Jersey, women's tournaments in 1985. Unfortunately, she lost in each final. No one except hard-core tennis fans paid much attention to the smaller tournaments, though. Most people watched the Grand Slam events.

That year, fans watched 17-year-old Boris Becker become the youngest man ever to win Wimbledon. Boris, who had barely been on the men's tour a year, beat Kevin Curren, 6-3, 6-7, 7-6, 6-4, in the Wimbledon final.

But at the U.S. Open, Steffi showed the tennis world that she might be just as tough as her friend, the men's Wimbledon champ. Steffi played in one of the most exciting Open matches ever. She had made it to the quarterfinals, where she faced Pam Shriver, an American who was then ranked Number 3 in the world.

They played on a hot September day. The temperature was nearly 100 degrees and the humidity was close to 100 percent. It felt like it was still August in New York City.

The U.S. Open is played at the National Tennis Center in Flushing Meadows, New York. It's probably one of the worst places to play tennis in the world. Flushing Meadows is in Queens, one of the five boroughs of New York City.

The Tennis Center is only a short distance from LaGuardia Airport. Planes fly directly over the tennis courts, distracting players with a thunderous roar. And when jets aren't taking off, the rattle-rattle-rattle of the nearby subway is loud enough to be heard on the courts.

Of course, the distractions didn't bother 16-year-old Steffi. As 6,000 spectators watched, Steffi won the first set—in a tiebreaker, which is used in tournaments after the score reaches 6-6. Pam won the second set—also in a tiebreaker. In the third set, Pam was up 5-3 and it looked as though Steffi might lose. But Steffi's killer instincts took over. She evened the score at 6-6. Steffi used her wicked forehand and slicing backhand to win the tiebreaker—and the match—with a score of 7-4.

When the match was over, Pam's and Steffi's shirts were drenched with sweat. The match had lasted 2 hours and 45 minutes. It was the first match in women's Open tennis ever to go the maximum 39 games allowed under current tennis rules. They played each set to 6-6, and then played a tiebreaker at the end of each.

Journalists crowded around Steffi afterwards. "Were you nervous, Steffi?" they asked. "Well, not really," she replied. “Were you tired?” “Well, not really,” she answered again. “Do you like being the focus of so much attention, Steffi?” they asked. “Well, not really,” she replied, as tersely as before.

Pam, meanwhile, went to the sidelines, where she started sobbing and hugging her coach, Don Candy. When she pulled herself together, she said, “It was unbelievable. I couldn’t have put in more effort, and it was two points too few.”

Steffi’s efforts were such a thrill to the West German journalists that they decided to broadcast the last 25 minutes of her match live. Hordes of West German reporters had come to New York to follow Boris Becker, the Wimbledon champ. But Becker lost in the fourth round, and after that the West Germans followed Steffi. Steffi’s victory advanced her to the semifinals, where she would play Martina Navratilova for the first time ever. Martina had lost only four matches the entire year, and Steffi acknowledged that she didn’t have much of a chance. “I want to try to win,” said Steffi. “Still, it won’t be that easy.”

In the semifinal game, Martina beat Steffi. Steffi was sorry she had lost to Martina, but she was happy to have made it so far in the U.S. Open.

Pam and Steffi played each other again that year, in October, at a tournament in Filderstadt, West Germany. During the match, Pam was clearly out to get back at Steffi. Pam made fun of her, sticking out her tongue and waving good-bye to Steffi's balls when they bounced out of bounds. Pam won, 6-4, 6-3.

Steffi was furious. She felt that the officials at the tournament should have prevented Pam from making fun of her. She vowed that she would never play in Filderstadt again—and she hasn't. One good thing did come out of the tournament, however. Because she made it to the final, Steffi rose in the rankings. She was now the sixth-best player in the world.

To her fellow West Germans, Steffi was already Number 1. When she returned home after the U.S. Open, she was hounded by autograph seekers and flooded with fan letters. When Steffi wanted a moment of peace at home, she had to take the phone off the hook. All of a sudden, she couldn't go anywhere in West Germany without being recognized. Steffi wasn't happy about this development—she is a shy and private girl. And although she had been preparing herself to reach the top, she wasn't prepared to be a celebrity.

Steffi's father saw that she needed a break. After Steffi finished the tennis season in November, she stayed at home in Brühl for almost four months. She didn't practice as much as usual, and she didn't go to any tournaments. This was not because she didn't want to, but because her father wouldn't let her. He didn't want Steffi to lose her love for tennis. He didn't want her to burn out. "Everybody talks about burnout, but if you have a good coach and rest between tournaments, it helps," Steffi says. "I think it makes me a steady player, too. I am not losing in the first round."

Even now, Steffi's father makes her spend at least two weeks every year away from tennis. During that time, she's not allowed to even touch a racket. "It's tough keeping my hands off a racket," she says. "During my time off, there will be three and a half hours every day when I have nothing to do. After a week, I get crazy."

Mr. Graf knew the kind of price that Steffi would have to pay for her success. The more successful she became, the less her life would be her own. And he could also see that she would be very successful.

4

Moving in on Martina

At the beginning of 1986, Steffi set two goals for herself. First, she wanted to hold a steady spot in the Top 10. Second, she wanted to win her first major tournament.

She started the year slowly, as she often does. In February, she made it to the finals of the Lipton tournament in Boca Raton. Steffi had made it to the semifinals of this same tournament the year before, only to lose to Chris Evert. And it was Chris Evert, then 31 years old, who got the best of Steffi again. Steffi was impatient to win and made too many mistakes. Chris beat her, 6-4, 6-2.

But Chris was quick to praise her young opponent. "Steffi has all the shots and moves beautifully," Chris told reporters. "She has that huge forehand and a slice backhand that give her a style that's all her own."

Even though Steffi lost, being in the finals of the Lipton tournament moved her up to the Number 4 spot. Steffi was happy that she had risen so high in the rankings, but she responded to the news with an honesty that has become her trademark. "There are players who are better than me," she said. "I have a lot of improving to do, and would just like to stay in the Top 10 this year."

Steffi and Chris met again in April for the final match of the Family Circle Magazine Cup on Hilton Head, an island off the coast of South Carolina. It was the sixth time the two had played each other. This time, Steffi was more patient. She wanted to beat Chris at her own game, pounding groundstrokes from the baseline, waiting for Chris to make an error. It worked. Steffi beat Chris 6-4, 7-5. She had won her first major tournament!

"It was nice that Steffi won her first tournament," Chris told reporters. Then Chris smiled, and added, "Unfortunately, it was against me."

Winning her first tournament gave Steffi the confidence she needed to win more. And win more is exactly what she did. She extended her Hilton Head victory to four consecutive wins. A week after she beat Chris, Steffi won her second tournament when she beat her countrywoman, Claudia Kohde-Kilsch, 6-4, 5-7, 7-6 in the final of the Sunkist Championship on Amelia Island, Florida.

Steffi won even though she was penalized a point by tournament officials. Officials thought Steffi's dad was coaching her from the sidelines, which is not allowed in women's tennis, and they gave a point to Claudia. Steffi and her father disagreed. "He was cheering me on and, through your emotions, you move your hands," Steffi said. "I didn't recognize any signals."

Whether or not she recognized any signals, the officials were still convinced that Steffi's father was coaching her. The press thought that Steffi's father had too much control over her, and that he stuck his nose where it didn't belong. To them, this sideline coaching was just one more example of it. Steffi was upset that her father was being criticized.

Next, Steffi went to Indianapolis for the U.S. Open Clay Courts Championship. There, she defeated 15-year-old Gabriela Sabatini of Argentina, 2-6, 7-6, 6-4. Tennis fans adored Gaby, as Gabriela is often called. With her photogenic smile and sparkling brown eyes, she could be a model as easily as a tennis player. Wherever Gaby went, the press and the cameras followed. They touted Gaby as the next Number 1, while ignoring Steffi's accomplishments. That was fine with Steffi. "I don't mind all the attention Gaby gets," said Steffi. "I like it more when the attention is on the other players."

Steffi's father agreed. "We have a different mentality," he said. "We Germans, or maybe just we Grafs, are quiet. We like to have people talk about Boris and Gabriela. Then, we can work much better in peace and quiet."

Gabriela was small-time, though, compared to Steffi's next victim, Martina. Steffi and Martina squared off in the final of the German Open in May. Steffi had always wanted to beat Martina. The two had played three times before, and Steffi had never won even a set from her then 29-year-old rival.

At the German Open, Steffi was particularly hungry for a victory, and she had the advantage of a sympathetic crowd because the Open was held at the Rot-Weiss Tennis Club in West Berlin.

For 65 minutes, Martina flailed helplessly at the ball as

Steffi sent one sledgehammer forehand after another flying across the net. The West German crowd cheered wildly as their 16-year-old *wunderkind* [*VOON-der-kint*], or wonder kid, won, 6-2, 6-3. Martina was stunned and left the court in tears. "It was an execution," Martina said.

"Martina is still Number 1 in the world," Steffi said. "And Chris is still unchallengeable for Number 2 when she plays faultlessly. Before, I used to be a little bit scared of playing Martina and Chris. Now, it's their turn to be scared of me."

Reporters asked Steffi about the French Open. Steffi had now defeated every top-ranked player. Did she think she could win on the clay courts in Paris?

"I don't want to put extra pressure on myself," she said, trying to avoid the question altogether. "I am going to relax at my home . . . where I can have all the peace I want."

Steffi went home to see her family and get ready for the French Open, which was only two weeks away. At home, she practiced with her father for four hours a day. She also lifted weights, ran and jumped rope with weights on her ankles to improve her foot speed. This may sound like a lot of work, but it was all part of her usual fitness routine.

When Steffi arrived in France, she modestly predicted that she would make it as far as the quarterfinals. And that is exactly what she did. The fact that she had guessed right didn't make her feel any better when she lost. On a sunny Paris day, Steffi fell to Czechoslovakian Hana Mandlikova. Steffi had won the first set, 6-2. In the second set, she was ahead 5-4, one game away from victory, and was serving for the match point. Steffi missed her first serve, which meant trouble because Hana likes to attack on the second serve. Hana did just that. Steffi lost the set—and the match.

When the match was finished, Steffi's father came down onto the court. "You did your best," he said to Steffi, while giving her a hug. Despite her father's support, Steffi burst into tears as she left the court. It was frustrating for her to be such a good player and not win a Grand Slam event.

While she was at the French Open, Steffi picked up a virus that she couldn't shake. It was so bad that Steffi had to withdraw from Wimbledon, which began on June 23, three weeks after her loss in the French Open and 9 days after her seventeenth birthday. "Steffi is very sick," her dad said. "She was looking forward to Wimbledon. She is very down and disappointed about this." He added, though, that Steffi would be well in time to play at the Federation Cup in Prague, Czechoslovakia, at the end of July.

While Steffi was at home resting, her friend Boris Becker went on to win his second straight Wimbledon. He had beaten Ivan Lendl, the Number 1 player, in the final, 6-4, 6-3, 7-5. Lendl didn't have a chance against the energetic 18-year-old. Boris was amazed at his success. He was already a hero in Germany, having received more than 60,000 fan letters since his last Wimbledon victory. "Nobody can really believe it," Boris said.

Steffi flew to Prague in July. She had recovered from her virus and was ready to play for the West German team at the Federation Cup Tournament. After she had won two matches, though, a freak accident kept her from playing. A strong wind blew over a table with a sun umbrella on it. The umbrella fell onto Steffi's right foot, breaking her big toe. Doctors examined Steffi and placed her right foot in a cast. Like most casts, it was too big to fit under a tennis shoe, and too clumsy for running around a tennis court. Besides, the best way for her toe to heal was to keep unnecessary pressure off of it.

That wasn't a very good way to show the world that

she was the Number 3 player. One thing after another had kept her off the court. At the U.S. Open, though, she would show the world that she deserved her ranking . . . and maybe more.

Steffi had a special shoe built that would protect her right toe while she was playing. She warmed up for the U.S. Open by winning a tournament in Mahwah, New Jersey. Her opponent was Molly Van Nostrand of New York. Molly didn't cause Steffi nearly as many problems as the wind did. At times, the wind gusted up to 40 miles an hour at courtside. Still, Steffi won, 7-5, 6-1. At the awards ceremony, Steffi was offered a drink of champagne out of the tournament cup. "My first drink!" Steffi said. No one wanted to tell the champ that she was four years too young to drink in New Jersey.

At the start of the U.S. Open, it looked as if Steffi might continue to win. She insisted to reporters that there was no way she could win the Open at the age of 17. Reporters persisted. "Steffi, you are so good," they'd say. "How can you tell us you won't win it?" Steffi smiled. "I am not always saying what I believe," she said. She knew she had a chance.

Steffi played so hurriedly it was as if she had illegally parked her car outside the National Tennis Center. She defeated Susan Mascarin of the U.S., 6-0, 6-1, in 40 minutes. In the second round, she sent Andrea Temesvari of Hungary packing in 39 minutes. Temesvari, ranked 40th, got so frustrated during the match that she swung her racket at a row of courtside flowers, taking the blossoms off several plants. The match was delayed because Andrea had to pluck the petals from her strings.

"I think it's maybe not such good preparation for the end of the tournament to have such short matches," Graf said, who stomps her feet impatiently during rest periods. "But I like to get things done fast, win points and matches as quick as I can."

Steffi's father liked her to win quickly, too. Shorter matches cause less stress on her mind and her body. Steffi is less likely to get injured when she isn't playing long, drawn-out matches. "That is her mentality on the court," Mr. Graf said. "She is aggressive, likes to make the point quickly. For her body, it's much better."

Steffi made it to the quarterfinals, where she defeated Bonnie Gadusek of the United States. Martina had defeated Pam Shriver in another quarterfinal, and would face Steffi in the semifinal.

Steffi was confident that she could win the match. "Most players go into their matches with Martina afraid and they just try to play some good games," Steffi said. "That is not what I want to do. I want to beat her."

"I'm glad she's confident enough to say that and believe it," Martina replied. "I had that attitude when I was young. It doesn't scare me." Martina couldn't wait to face Steffi. She said that she was "pumped up like I've never been for a semifinal."

As the match got underway on a Friday afternoon, the fans knew they were going to see a tight match. But Martina was ahead, 4-1, in the first set when the unpredictable New York skies opened up and it poured. The game was delayed for five hours before officials decided to postpone it until the next day.

On Saturday, Martina finished off the first set, 6-1. The next set wasn't so easy. Steffi was determined to win and nothing could break her concentration. Steffi took Martina to a tiebreaker in the second set, and then won the tiebreaker, 7-3.

Steffi had found a way to battle Martina's volleying. She lobbed balls out of Martina's reach, forcing her into the backcourt. When that wouldn't work, Steffi sent the ball directly back at Martina to try and intimidate her. Martina was impressed. "My mind was set," Martina said. "I had to come to the net and make her keep hitting those wonderful shots."

The third set went to a tiebreaker as well, thrilling all the fans. It is very rare that a women's game is so close. Even the men tennis players, who say they are often bored by women's tennis, watched the end of the match. "You should have heard it," Boris Becker said. "Maniac screaming on every point."

The tiebreaker went to 8-all. Either Steffi or Martina had to pull ahead by two points to win. Steffi decided to take a chance. She made a rare trip to the net—and missed.

Martina needed only one more point. She bounced up and down, holding one finger in the air. "One more!" she yelled. "One more!" Martina then served to Steffi's backhand. Steffi hit it—straight into the net. She had lost the match, and was out of the U.S. Open.

The other women players, the press and the fans, though, were delighted to have watched such a close match. "For women's tennis, it was as if we had died and gone to heaven," said Pam Shriver.

Steffi, of course, was terribly disappointed. "It was so close that the score doesn't matter. I just wanted to win." She then added that "Martina is not that much better than everybody else. I'm getting much closer now. I have to improve my serve much more and then I think it's going to be a much tougher match for her."

Steffi wasn't being bitter with those comments. She is honest with her feelings. If asked to give her opinion of a player, Steffi almost always replies frankly, but not with bad intentions.

Minutes after the match ended, Steffi's father rushed her to the airport to a catch a flight to Tokyo. Steffi was playing in the Pan Pacific Championships in Tokyo a week later. She likes getting to her destination early to have time to adjust.

Martina stayed around. She chatted with reporters for a while about the match. Martina was delighted with her victory, and she could see the possibility of a new era in women's tennis.

"Steffi is a terrific player. I hope she doesn't get much better," Martina said. "If she does, I'll quit."

5

A New Era

In the fall of 1986, Steffi appeared on a West German television game show. She ended up losing and had to come up with her own penalty. She decided that she would give a bouquet of flowers to the next player who defeated her in a tournament.

Steffi won 17 consecutive matches before she lost. Her loss came to Martina Navratilova in the finals of the Virginia Slims Championships that November in Madison Square Garden. During the awards ceremony at the Garden, Steffi presented Martina with a bunch of flowers.

"That was nice," Martina said. "She didn't have to do that in public."

With that gesture, Steffi had proved that she could keep a promise and had shown her respect for the Number 1 player. It wouldn't be long, though, before Steffi would steal away Martina's ranking. "After that match [at the U.S. Open], everyone knew," says Pam Shriver. "It was only a matter of time until Steffi took over."

The Steffi Graf era was about to begin. Steffi had come along and upset the order, as young players always do. Her arrival, though, meant the departure of the Chris-and-Martina era, one of the most celebrated in women's tennis.

Chris and Martina had been around for a long time. Tennis fans loved their games, their personalities and their rivalry. They had been on top for so long that people could hardly remember what it was like before them. Chris and Martina had held the Number 1 spot, at different times, for 12 years. Tracy Austin had snuck in for a brief stay at the top in 1980, but she was the only one, and she didn't last long.

From 1975 to 1982, Chris and Martina alternated holding the top spot. From 1982 to 1987, Martina was Number 1 alone. During that time, Chris was always second. She was the only player in professional tennis who had a chance of knocking Martina off her throne.

Tennis fans had grown accustomed to seeing either Chris or Martina in the finals of a Grand Slam tournament. The most popular games were when Chris and Martina played against one another. Their rivalry went a long way back.

Chris had burst onto the tennis scene as a 16-year-old in the 1971 U.S. Open. She upset a string of older players before finally being defeated in the semifinals. By the time she was 18, she was already a star. Fans, especially Americans, adored her. Chris was pretty, with ribbons in her ponytail, and as American as apple pie. But when she picked up her racket, she was no longer just another teenager. Her mental concentration was stronger than her two-handed backhand.

Martina was two years younger than Chris. She had grown up thousands of miles away in Czechoslovakia, an Eastern European country then under communist rule. She yearned for the freedoms of the United States, and Chris was in many ways a symbol of that freedom. Martina idolized Chris. "My goal," said Martina, "was for her to remember my name. She didn't know me from Adam." Chris and

Martina were two very different people who shared a great love—and great talent—for tennis.

Chris and Martina first played against one another in Akron, Ohio, in March 1973. Chris was 18 and Martina was 16. They were playing in the first round of a tournament sponsored by the Junior League, a women's organization. Chris won, 7-6, 6-3, but she never forgot Martina's name. The two met many times after that. Chris dominated their early competition, winning 25 of 36 matches in the 1970s. Martina took control from 1980 to 1985, winning 24 of 31 matches. She beat Chris 13 consecutive times from 1982 to 1985.

"No one had ever come along and beat me 13 straight matches like she did," Chris said.

Tennis fans loved to watch the two play each other because their styles were so different. Chris, looking cool and elegant, would stand at the baseline waiting for Martina to make a mistake. Martina, on the other hand, was a serve-and-volley player. She would whip up a brutal serve, and then rush the net to volley.

Martina was always much more emotional than Chris. When Martina was mad, she was fuming. When she was happy, she couldn't contain her joy. When she lost, she wanted to cry.

Despite the differences and the competition between the two women, they became close friends (something Steffi has always found hard to do with *her* competition). "The most remarkable thing is that we became better friends through it all," Martina said. "We realized we can be close and still try to beat each other's brains out."

They respected one another, as tennis players *and* as people. Chris might have slaughtered Martina on the court, but she always visited her in the locker room later. They would talk about the match, and the winner would console the loser.

They had fun together, when their competition wasn't too intense. "At the French Open in 1975, we had a ball together, hitting the restaurants, having picnics in our hotel rooms," Martina said. "Chris beat me in the finals, and we won the doubles together."

They learned to trust one another. When Martina decided to defect from Czechoslovakia in 1975, she told very few people. Chris was one of them. When Chris divorced her husband, John Lloyd, in 1987, Martina was there to comfort her. "Martina invited me to stay with her in Aspen, Colorado, where she has a home," Chris said. "I was going through a very painful period in my life. That's when we started opening up to each other."

Each woman made her own contribution to the game. Chris brought tennis a two-handed backhand and a more feminine image. Before Chris, many women tennis players were viewed as masculine. But Chris showed the world that an athlete could be feminine *and* competitive.

Martina brought power and strength to the game. And she revolutionized the way women trained for tennis. In the early 1980s, Martina began to run, lift weights and play basketball. Before then, few women players were serious about fitness. When other players saw the improvements in Martina's game, they followed her example. Now, most of the women on the tour follow a regular fitness routine.

When Steffi was growing up, she looked up to Chris and Martina. And when she turned professional, Chris and Martina were firmly established as the leaders of women's tennis. They were the game's hottest players, as well as its most respected spokeswomen.

In 1987, Steffi ended their reign. She started the year

taller and stronger. She had grown to the size she is today, 5'9", 130 pounds. And now, more than ever, Steffi wanted to become Number 1.

To do that, Steffi had to improve certain parts of her game. She needed to have a net game, a stronger serve and a more reliable backhand. Steffi's father hired Pavel Slozil, a Czechoslovakian who once played on the men's tour, to work with Steffi. Steffi spent December 1986 and January 1987 working on improving her game. She skipped the Australian Open in January.

Pavel had Steffi serve one ball after another, until she came up with a knee-bending, ball-whamming serve that looked almost as fierce as Boris Becker's. Becker has been nicknamed "Boom-Boom" because of his wicked serve. Martina had always had the toughest serve on the women's tour, but Steffi was starting to come close.

Steffi also needed to improve her backhand so that opponents wouldn't be so eager to hit to it. It had always been considered her weakest stroke, and opponents had hit to it as often as possible. Pavel worked on putting a topspin on Steffi's backhand. A topspin happens when the ball is spinning in the same direction it is traveling. The ball dips downward after it clears the net, making it harder to volley.

Pavel hit ball after ball after ball to Steffi's backhand, until she had a stroke that was reliable. Her backhand isn't as overpowering as her forehand, but it is no longer a weakness.

Steffi also worked on her net game with Pavel. She would try to serve-and-volley. Or she would stand at the net while he hit to her. Still, Steffi remained reluctant to come to the net. She could control the game much better from the baseline, so there wasn't much reason to come forward. She was hesitant at the net, and tended to make mistakes.

At some point, she may still have to improve her net game. But in early 1987, she made just the changes that were absolutely needed in her game.

Steffi joined the tour again in February, in time for the Virginia Slims of Florida tournament held in Boca Raton. She defeated Helena Suvoka of Czechoslovakia in the finals.

The victory moved her from the Number 3 to the Number 2 spot. Steffi was one step closer to her goal. She was also on the verge of dethroning both queens of the court. Chris had been bumped to the Number 3 spot.

The week after the Virginia Slims tournament, Steffi

had to face both Chris *and* Martina, although not at the same time. They were all playing in the Lipton tournament, also in Florida. Steffi faced Martina in the semifinal game, and her improved strokes were a success.

The two played on a very windy day, and the gusts caused Martina problems with her game. Steffi beat her, 6-3, 6-2. But it wasn't just the wind that defeated Martina—Steffi's backhand helped. "The backhand was my most important shot today," Steffi said.

Martina thought Steffi's whole game was impressive. "Today she was the best player in the world," Martina said. "And she will be until I play her again." Martina was not going to take this defeat lying down.

Then Steffi played Chris in the final. Chris was coming back from a six-month layoff from tennis. She had been recuperating from an injured knee. But Steffi didn't keep Chris on the court for long. She needed only 58 minutes to beat Chris, 6-2, 6-2. "Steffi played better than I had expected," said Chris. "And she plays like she is in a hurry to get off the court."

Like Pam Shriver, Chris could see what was coming. "I don't want to predict who's going to finish Number 1 this year," she said. "Whoever it is will have their work cut out for them. There's no reason why Steffi can't win all the major tournaments. She will be very, very hard to beat this year."

Steffi was encouraged. "I never thought I'd be where I am now at 17," she said. "Now, I feel I can say I am Number 2. But beating Chris and Martina in three days makes this my biggest tournament win ever."

Steffi continued to win. She won six straight tournaments before the French Open began. Martina, on the other hand, could do nothing but lose. When the French Open began in May, Martina hadn't won a single tournament that year. She couldn't imagine that things could get any worse. Martina had been having trouble with one of her feet all year, and she had been having trouble with her coach, Mike Estep. She decided to try a new coach, but had trouble finding one until late January.

It was overcast and stormy in Paris for the French Open. The weather reflected Martina's mood. Paris is known as a romantic and beautiful city in the spring. In truth, it is often cold and rainy, especially during the French Open.

The Open is held in Paris's Roland Garros Stadium,

which is named after a pilot who fought in World War I. The stadium is on the western edge of Paris, set against a backdrop of the Paris skyline, with flowers, trees and rolling hills everywhere. Many tennis fans think that Roland Garros is in the most beautiful setting of any stadium.

The stadium is most famous for its red clay courts. The French Open is the only Grand Slam tournament that is played on clay. The clay is made of a special crushed brick from the village of Hermenon, which is about 50 miles from Paris.

Playing on clay is different from playing on any other surface. The clay slows down the bounce of the ball, and makes strategy more important than speed. Steffi's game is well suited to clay. She is an aggressive baseliner, cleverly attacking with groundstrokes from the back of the court. Martina's game, however, is faster and less suited to clay. She relies on hitting fast shots from the net—so fast they can't be returned. On clay, those shots are slower and aren't as difficult to reach and return.

Steffi's strategic play on clay helped her move quickly through the rounds. She beat Gabriela Sabatini in the semifinal and advanced to the final, where she would play

Martina. The day of the final was eight days before Steffi's eighteenth birthday.

Martina's confidence was low. She thought the problem might be her racket. She put down the Yonex racket she is paid to endorse, and she painted a Dunlop model (which Steffi uses) black to look like her Yonex. Martina might have had a chance against Steffi *if* she were playing her best tennis. Instead, Martina made costly mistakes.

Steffi took the first set, 6-4, and then Martina won the next set, 6-4. In the third set, Martina hit more and more to Steffi's backhand. Steffi returned the backhands by sending them flying past Martina and landing just inside the sideline. Steffi had pulled ahead, 7-6, and Martina was serving. Steffi was ready to fight for the last game, but she didn't have to. Martina double-faulted.

That wasn't a very exciting way for Steffi to win her first Grand Slam event. She had worked hard for the victory, but she ended up winning because of her opponent's errors. "I'm happy and sorry I won the match," Steffi said. "I'm sorry for those double faults. If she had not double-faulted, I don't think I would have won."

Martina was appalled by her loss. But she wouldn't

give up that easily. She still wanted the world to think of her as the best woman player. "Don't try to dethrone me," she pleaded with the press after her loss.

Steffi had become the youngest woman ever to win the French Open. (That record was later broken by 17-year-old Aranxta [*ah-RAHN-cha*] Sanchez Vicario in 1989.) Steffi won $180,000 for her victory. But she still didn't have the Number 1 spot. "It is every tennis player's dream to be Number 1," Steffi said. "There are more important things in life, but I am sure going to try."

When Steffi returned home to Brühl, a parade of local fans greeted her. They carried signs to show Steffi how much they adored her. Not all of the attention was good, though. A disturbed "fan" sent her a jar of marmalade that was laced with poison.

Steffi became almost single-minded in her pursuit of the top ranking in women's tennis. She had to concentrate on her game, so she didn't have time for socializing or dating. The press was beginning to wonder whether it wasn't time for Steffi to find a boyfriend. But Steffi wasn't ready to make that kind of commitment. "There is no time," said Steffi's father. "She wants the tennis too much. She could not share herself with another person."

Mr. Graf liked to tease Steffi about boys. A reporter from *The Washington Post* was interviewing Steffi in 1987 when her father started to joke with her. (Steffi's father usually watches over all her interviews.)

"No husband for you, right?" he asked Steffi. "Not so long as I am your father."

Steffi rolled her eyes up, as though he'd said this thousands of times before, and laughed.

"Okay, I tell you what," Steffi's dad said. "You can have a husband . . . in your next life."

But Steffi simply didn't have the time for close friendships or for boys. Her closest friends were her father, mother and brother. "Steffi has one thing on her mind," Steffi's father said before the 1987 French Open. "She has no time for a friend. If I have to tell her that she can't go to discos or that she has to be in bed by 9 P.M., it's no good. She must want to do this herself. So far, she does."

"I am not different from anyone else," Steffi insisted. "I want to be normal and do normal things. People ask about boys. They make a big thing of Becker having a girlfriend. But for me, right now, it is impossible because of the travel and I am so young. Later, it will be okay, I am sure."

It wasn't easy trying to stay friends with the kids she had gone to school with. Boris Becker had the same problem. He wasn't as single-minded about tennis as Steffi, but he found that people treated him differently after he had become a tennis star. "Suddenly all my friends saw me as the Wimbledon champion," Boris told *Time* magazine. "So I lost them. 'Hey, wake up,' I'd try to say. 'I'm the one you sat in school with.' But they kept on being too nice to me for the wrong reasons. Strangers always ask if I've changed, but I think everyone else changed. It's sad."

Steffi saw how Boris Becker's life had changed since he had become a tennis star. Boris was followed everywhere by the press. If he sneezed, it was in the newspaper headlines. If he went to dinner with a woman, it was in the headlines. When he moved to Monte Carlo, a city in Monaco, it was in the headlines.

Boris wasn't like Steffi. He was much more public with his emotions. "Like all artists, Boris has to bring something extra to his work," said Boris's manager, Ion Tiriac. "Germanic people are supposed to be stable and square, but you would think that Boris was born in Italy. He always lives on his emotions."

Steffi was glad that the press paid more attention to Boris than to her, but she could see that it wasn't easy on her friend.

Steffi didn't mind that she couldn't go out or have time for a boyfriend. She loved playing tennis and wanted to be Number 1 so much that almost any sacrifice seemed worth it. It was the life she had chosen, and it didn't seem like a sacrifice at all to Steffi.

"I have my tennis as I want it," she said. "At the moment, this is the perfect life."

6

On Top of the World

Steffi only needed to win one more tournament to become the best woman player in the world. That tournament was Wimbledon. She knew that she was a long shot to make it to the final game because the last time she had played in a grass-court tournament was the 1985 Wimbledon tournament when she had lost to the British player Jo Durie. Steffi had missed the 1986 event because of illness. And in her whole career, she had played only three grass-court tournaments.

And then there was Martina, who would be a tough opponent. After all her defeats, Martina wanted to prove that she still reigned on the courts she considered home. A *New*

Heinz Kluetmeier/Sports Illustrated

Steffi and Boris Becker (far right) posed for a picture with the German Tennis Federation Program in Lieman in 1976.

Fast Facts About Boris Becker

• Boris was born on November 22, 1967, in Lieman, West Germany.

• Boris played both soccer and tennis as a young boy. At 12, he gave up soccer to concentrate on tennis.

• He was the West German junior champion three years in a row—1983, 1984 and 1985.

• In 1985 when he was 17, Boris became the youngest man ever to win Wimbledon. He won the championship again in 1986 and 1989.

• Boris won the U.S. Open in 1989.

• He has earned over 5 million dollars during his career.

• Boris now lives in Monte Carlo, Monaco and Lieman, West Germany.

Bill Frakes/Sports Illustrated

Steffi, lounging by the pool with a cool fruit drink.

Fast Facts About the Australian Open

What: A Grand Slam Event

When: January

Where: The National Tennis Center
Melbourne, Australia

Surface: Hard Court

Roger Gould/Sports Illustrated

Steffi's powerful serve helped her win the 1988 Australian Open. This was her first step toward winning the Golden Grand Slam.

James Drake/Sports Illustrated

Steffi served up a 6-0, 6-0 win over Natalia Zvereva in the 1988 French Open final. The match lasted just 32 minutes.

Gerard Vandystadt/Sports Illustrated

In 1988, Steffi became the youngest woman to win the French Open, a record that was broken the very next year by 17-year-old Aranxta Sanchez Vicario of Spain.

Gerard Vandystadt/Sports Illustrated

Steffi, posing with her winner's trophy, was victorious at the 1988 French Open. It was her second step on the road to the Golden Grand Slam.

Martina played Chris Evert in the semifinals at Wimbledon in 1988.

Fast Facts About Martina Navratilova

• Martina was born on October 18, 1956, in Prague, Czechoslovakia.

• She became an American citizen on July 21, 1981.

• Martina has won 17 Grand Slam singles titles during her career. She has won the Australian Open three times, the French Open twice, Wimbledon eight times and the U.S. Open four times.

• She set a women's record by winning six consecutive Wimbledon singles titles from 1982 to 1987.

Steve Powell/Sports Illustratd

In 1988, Steffi broke Martina's streak of six Wimbledon singles titles by winning 5-7, 6-2, 6-1.

Fast Facts About Wimbledon

What:	A Grand Slam Event
When:	Late June/Early July
Where:	The All England Tennis and Croquet Club, London, England
Surface:	Grass

Steve Powell/Sports Illustrated

Steffi had a silver-plated victory on the grass courts at Wimbledon in 1988.

Jacquelin Duvoisin/Sports Illustrated

Despite a "Stop Graf" movement by the other players, Steffi won the 1988 U.S. Open—and the Grand Slam. She was only the fifth player ever to win the Slam.

Walter Iooss, Jr./Sports Illustrated

Gabriela Sabatini faced Steffi in the final of the 1988 U.S. Open. After a hesitant start, Steffi beat her, 6-3, 3-6, 6-1.

Fast Facts about the U.S. Open

What: A Grand Slam Event

When: Late August/Early Sept

Where: National Tennis Center
Flushing, New York

Surface: Hard court

Walter Iooss, Jr./Sports Illustrated

Steffi showed how powerful her game is at the 1988 U.S. Open. Her forehand is so forceful that reporters call it "a weapon." Steffi beat Gabriela in the final to win the Grand Slam.

Tommy Hindley/Sports Illustrated

Steffi made her Grand Slam golden by winning the gold medal in tennis at the 1988 Olympics in Seoul, South Korea.

Fast Facts About Chris Evert

• Chris was born on December 21, 1954, in Fort Lauderdale, Florida.

• Chris has won 157 singles titles, more than any other professional woman tennis player in history.

• She has won18 Grand Slam singles titles—two Australian Opens, seven French Opens, three Wimbledons and six U.S. Opens.

• Chris married Alpine skier Andy Mill on July 30, 1988.

• She retired from professional tennis after she played in the 1989 U.S. Open.

• Chris lives in Boca Raton, Florida, and Aspen, Colorado.

Caryn Levy/Sports Illustrated

Steffi's brother Michael, Steffi, her mother Heidi and her father Peter remain close, despite Steffi's demanding career.

Caryn Levy/Sports Illustrated

Even her famous two-handed backhand couldn't help Chris Evert in the final of the 1989 Virginia Slims Tournament in Boca Raton, Florida. Steffi beat Chris in the final, 4-6, 6-2, 6-3.

David Walberg/Sports Illustrated

Steffi's hitting coach since 1986, Pavel Slozil helped her develop an unstoppable serve and a powerful backhand.

Heinz Kluetmeier/Sports Illustrated

Steffi usually holds her emotions in better than she was able to at this tournament, which was held in West Germany in May 1989.

Heinz Kluetmeier/Sports Illustrated

Signing autographs is tougher than any match for Steffi. After a match in West Germany in May 1989, Steffi obliged many of her young fans.

Scoring Tennis

The rules of tennis were made up more than a hundred years ago, and they may seem a little strange now.

There are four units of scoring in tennis: point, game, set and match. Now, here's the part that's hard to figure out: a score of zero in tennis is called "love." When a player wins her first point, her score is 15. When she wins a second point, her score is 30. On the third point, the score is 40 and on the fourth, the player wins the game.

(continued)

Scoring Tennis (continued)

Of course, a player's opponent usually wins points too. When the score of a game is 40-40, it's called "deuce." At deuce, a player must win two consecutive points to win the game.

The first player to win six games wins the set. A set must be won, though, by at least two games. A player couldn't win if she was leading 6-5. She'd have to win one more game, making the score 7-5, to win the set.

The first player to win two sets out of three is the winner of the match.

Walter Iooss, Jr./Sports Illustrated

At the 1989 French Open, Steffi was expected to walk all over the young field—Martina and Chris were not there. However, the field was a lot more talented than anyone anticipated.

Bob Martin/Sports Illustrated

Steffi faced Monica Seles in the semifinal at the 1989 French Open. Monica is one of the best young players on the tour, and she took Steffi to three sets before Steffi won, 6-3, 3-6, 6-3.

Walter Iooss, Jr./Sports Illustrated

Steffi faced Aranxta Sanchez Vicario in the final of the 1989 French Open. Aranxta proved a tough opponent and dragged the match out for three hours before finally winning. Aranxta became the youngest woman ever to win the French Open. She was 17.

Walter Iooss, Jr./Sports Illustrated

Steffi and Aranxta hugged each other after their tough final match at the 1989 French Open.

Fast Facts About the French Open

What: A Grand Slam Event

When: Late May/Early June

Where: Roland Garros Stadium
Paris, France

Surface: Clay

Heinz Kluetmeier/Sports Illustrated

Determined to win at Wimbledon after her loss at the 1989 French Open, Steffi faced Martina in the final. Steffi won, 6-2, 6-7, 6-1.

Heinz Kluetmeier/Sports Illustrated

When Steffi and Boris won the 1989 Wimbledon championships, it was the first time since 1934 that the women's and men's winners both came from the same European country.

Tiebreaker

A tiebreaker is a special game that is played when a set is tied at six games apiece. Tiebreakers are always used in official tournament play.

A tiebreaker is usually a 12-point game. Each player takes turns serving, switching service after every two points. The first player to gain seven points wins the game—and the set. Of course, the player must win by two points.

Manny Millan/Sports Illustrated

The temperature on the court during the 1989 U.S. Open rose as high as 120 degrees. The muscles in Steffi's legs began to cramp and Steffi had to take time out during her match against Gabriela.

Manny Millan/Sports Illustrated

Manny Millan/Sports Illustrated

Steffi beat Martina at the 1989 U.S. Open, 3-6, 7-5, 6-1. Martina did not win a single Grand Slam tournament in the 1989 season.

Caryn Levy/Sports Illustrated

Jennifer Capriati, who is nearly seven years younger than Steffi, is considered one of the main threats to Steffi's Number 1 ranking in the coming years.

Manny Millan/Sports Illustrated

Steffi loves to play with her dogs when she is at home in West Germany.

Determining Tennis Rankings

The Women's International Tennis Association uses a point system to determine rankings. During a tournament every player is awarded points for each round she wins. She also receives "bonus" points for beating a high-ranked player. Players are awarded the most points for winning Grand Slam tournaments.

Suppose Steffi had beaten Martina in the final game of a Grand Slam tournament. Steffi would receive 350 points for winning the tournament and she would receive 52 points for beating Martina, the Number 2 player in the world.

All of Steffi's points would be added up for 52 weeks (one year) of tournament play. The total points would then be divided by the number of tournaments in which Steffi played.

STEFFI GRAF THE QUEST to be THE BEST
STEFFI GRAF GOT HER FIRST TENNIS RACKET WHEN SHE WAS NOT YET 4 YEARS OLD. THE RACKET WAS SAWED OFF SO LITTLE STEFFI COULD HOLD IT. NO ONE KNEW IT THEN, BUT THOSE FIRST TENNIS GAMES PLAYED RIGHT AT HOME WERE THE START OF SOMETHING BIG.
IF SHE KEEPS THIS UP SHE'S GOING TO WRECK THE WHOLE HOUSE!
BUT SHE LOVES TO PLAY! WHY DON'T I SET SOMETHING UP IN THE BASEMENT SO SHE CAN KEEP PRACTICING?
CRASH!
IN THE FALL OF 1982 STEFFI WAS 13 YEARS OLD AND ALREADY THE 12TH BEST PLAYER IN GERMANY. THAT'S WHEN SHE ALSO MADE A BIG ANNOUNCEMENT.
STEFFI HAS DECIDED TO BECOME A PROFESSIONAL TENNIS PLAYER!
PRESS

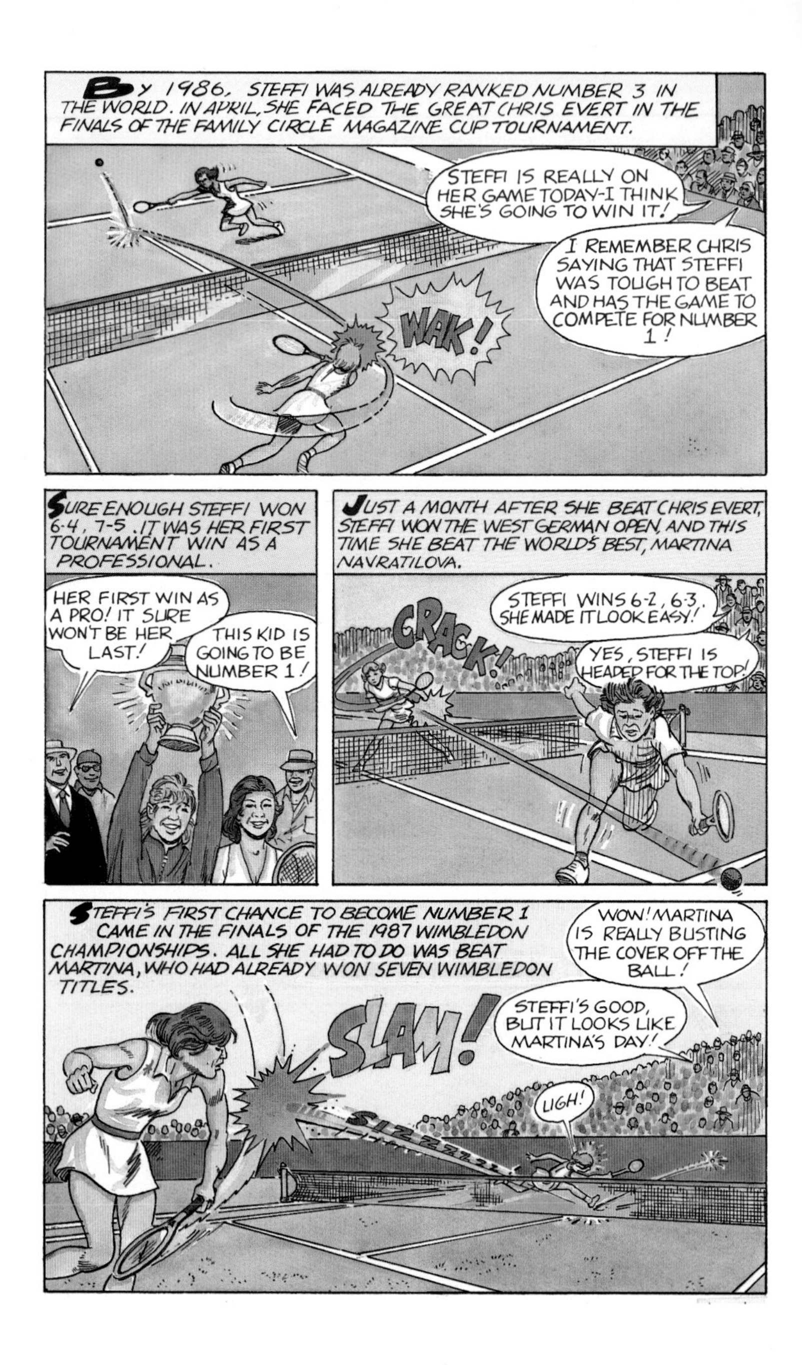
BY 1986, STEFFI WAS ALREADY RANKED NUMBER 3 IN THE WORLD. IN APRIL, SHE FACED THE GREAT CHRIS EVERT IN THE FINALS OF THE FAMILY CIRCLE MAGAZINE CUP TOURNAMENT.
STEFFI IS REALLY ON HER GAME TODAY-I THINK SHE'S GOING TO WIN IT!
I REMEMBER CHRIS SAYING THAT STEFFI WAS TOUGH TO BEAT AND HAS THE GAME TO COMPETE FOR NUMBER 1!
WAK!
SURE ENOUGH STEFFI WON 6-4, 7-5. IT WAS HER FIRST TOURNAMENT WIN AS A PROFESSIONAL.
HER FIRST WIN AS A PRO! IT SURE WON'T BE HER LAST!
THIS KID IS GOING TO BE NUMBER 1!
JUST A MONTH AFTER SHE BEAT CHRIS EVERT, STEFFI WON THE WEST GERMAN OPEN, AND THIS TIME SHE BEAT THE WORLD'S BEST, MARTINA NAVRATILOVA.
CRACK!
STEFFI WINS 6-2, 6-3. SHE MADE IT LOOK EASY!
YES, STEFFI IS HEADED FOR THE TOP!
STEFFI'S FIRST CHANCE TO BECOME NUMBER 1 CAME IN THE FINALS OF THE 1987 WIMBLEDON CHAMPIONSHIPS. ALL SHE HAD TO DO WAS BEAT MARTINA, WHO HAD ALREADY WON SEVEN WIMBLEDON TITLES.
WOW! MARTINA IS REALLY BUSTING THE COVER OFF THE BALL!
STEFFI'S GOOD, BUT IT LOOKS LIKE MARTINA'S DAY!
SLAM!
UGH!

SURE ENOUGH, IT WAS MARTINA'S DAY. SHE WAS STILL THE BETTER GRASS COURT PLAYER AND WON THE MATCH 7-5, 6-3.
IF SOMEONE WAS GOING TO BEAT ME TODAY, THEY'D HAVE TO BE A BETTER PLAYER!
EVEN THOUGH I LOST, IT WAS STILL AN UNBELIEVABLE THING FOR ME TO GO TO THE FINALS.
BUT STEFFI WAS GETTING CLOSER. SIX WEEKS AFTER WIMBLEDON SHE WAS IN THE FINALS OF THE VIRGINIA SLIMS TOURNAMENT IN LOS ANGELES. IT LOOKED AS THOUGH A WIN OVER CHRIS EVERT WOULD BRING HER TO THE TOP SPOT ON THE COMPUTER RANKINGS.
JUST RELAX OUT THERE TODAY! I FOUND OUT THAT EVEN IF YOU WIN, YOU WILL STILL BE RANKED NUMBER 2!
TAKING HER FATHER'S ADVICE, STEFFI RELAXED AND WON 6-3, 6-4.
STEFFI LOOKS UNBEATABLE, AS USUAL!
SHE'S WORKED SO HARD, SHE HAS TO BE NUMBER 1 SOON!
WAK!

AFTER GETTING HER TROPHY AND A HUG FROM LOS ANGELES MAYOR TOM BRADLEY, STEFFI GOT A BIG SURPRISE FROM HER FATHER.
CONGRATULATIONS STEFFI! YOU'RE NOW THE NUMBER 1 PLAYER IN THE WORLD!
BUT YOU SAID I'D STILL BE NUMBER 2, WIN OR LOSE.
I DIDN'T WANT TO TELL YOU BEFORE BECAUSE I DIDN'T WANT YOU TO FEEL THE PRESSURE. NOW YOU CAN REALLY RELAX — YOU'VE DONE IT!
SINCE BECOMING NUMBER 1, STEFFI HAS GOTTEN EVEN BETTER. DURING 1988 SHE WON ALL FOUR MAJOR CHAMPIONSHIPS AS WELL AS AN OLYMPIC GOLD MEDAL. THEY CALLED IT THE GOLDEN GRAND SLAM. IT WAS SOMETHING NEVER DONE BEFORE, YET MANY FEEL SHE IS GOOD ENOUGH TO DO IT AGAIN....
BEN BROWN

York Times reporter wrote that "the grass courts are like a security blanket to keep the doubts away" for Martina.

"Grass is my domain," Martina said. And she was right. Martina had won seven Wimbledon singles championships, five of them in a row. Her game was best suited to grass. On grass courts, the game is very fast, and Martina can blast a booming serve, then rush to the net to hit fast, tricky shots that are difficult to return.

Martina had the experience that Steffi lacked. "Martina has won so many times," said Steffi. "And at this stage, experience is so important. She is a big step ahead of me. When I think of Martina, I think of a great athlete, maybe the best player ever."

Still, Steffi had the confidence that Martina had lost. "I'm not as confident as I have been in years past," Martina said. "The game is there, the shots are there. At this point, it's all emotional."

"It would be different if Martina was being challenged by Chris," said Peggy Gossett, former director of public relations for the Women's International Tennis Association. "But Martina has held the Number 1 ranking for five years, and all of a sudden this kid comes out of nowhere to challenge her. No one has come on as strongly and as quickly as Steffi has. Maybe Martina is feeling the pressure."

Steffi and her father didn't let anyone know where they were staying in London during Wimbledon. Steffi worked out at a local tennis club, but no one knew which one. Steffi's father didn't want anyone to interrupt his daughter's concentration. She needed to have peace and quiet to prepare for the tournament.

The British press, which is particularly nosy, went crazy because they couldn't find Steffi. The headline of one London paper read, "My Daddy's No Monster." That, supposedly, was Steffi's response to her father's helping her find time alone. He was protecting her. "I don't think monster is the right word," Steffi's father said. "I just want what is best for Steffi, and sometimes I have to fight for it."

The secrecy paid off. Steffi advanced very quickly through the early rounds all the way to the finals. But Martina was waiting for her in Centre Court. Martina whipped up big serves to Steffi's backhand, and Steffi repeatedly hit them into the net. Steffi served well, but she was no match for Martina. Martina won, 7-5, 6-3.

"I had beaten *myself* a couple of times this year,"

Martina said, "but I wasn't going to let that happen here. If someone was going to beat me, they'd have to be a better player. At the French, I couldn't see myself winning the last point. Here, I couldn't see it ending any other way."

Martina was particularly thrilled with her victory because she had tied one record and set another. She tied Helen Wills Moody's record (set in 1938) of eight Wimbledon singles titles. And she set a record with her six consecutive singles championships. "I have a record that may stand forever," she said. "If it gets broken and I'm still alive, I'd like to be here."

Steffi wasn't upset by her loss. "It's an unbelievable thing, me going to the finals," she said, considering how little experience she had on grass courts.

Six weeks later, Steffi was in Los Angeles to play in the Virginia Slims tournament. Steffi was coming very close to taking over the Number 1 spot. All she thought she had to do was win this tournament.

But her father told her otherwise. "It's not possible for you to be Number 1 after this tournament," he said. "Even if you win, you'll still be Number 2."

Steffi faced Chris Evert in the final on August 16 at the

Manhattan Country Club in Los Angeles. The 6,000 spectators all seemed to be cheering for Chris and that was no help to Steffi. In the first game, Steffi played nervously. She made four errors, and Chris broke her serve twice. That means that Chris won two games in which Steffi was serving. If the server is playing well, she usually wins her service games.

Steffi pulled herself together, though, and won the first set, 6-3, and then took the match after winning the second set, 6-4.

Steffi shook hands with Chris. Then she looked around for her father, whom she always kisses after her matches. He was walking onto the court. When he reached his daughter, he kissed her on the forehead. "Congratulations," he said softly. "You're now the Number 1 player in the world."

"But you told me . . ."

"You're Number 1," he repeated. "I didn't tell you before because I didn't want you to feel the pressure."

Steffi thought about it for a minute. Then she hugged her father and broke into a smile.

"I can't stop smiling," Steffi told reporters. She was only 18 years old and already the best woman player in the world. "It feels great. I was very surprised. Being Number 1 before the U.S. Open. It's important to get to be Number 1 before the U.S. Open. Now I can really relax."

An official from the tournament presented Steffi and Chris with their checks, as Los Angeles mayor Tom Bradley stood by. The official gave Chris a check, and then a hug and a kiss. After receiving her check, Steffi said, "I'm a little disappointed. I didn't get a hug or a kiss." With that, Mayor Bradley grabbed the microphone. "Steffi, I wouldn't want to disappoint you," he said, and then he gave her a bear hug.

"We knew she'd be Number 1," Mr. Graf said. "We just didn't know it would come this soon." He was very proud of his daughter.

Steffi felt as though a huge burden had been lifted. Now that she was Number 1, she didn't have to keep fighting. She could relax a little.

"What are you going to do to celebrate?" a reporter asked.

"I'm heading for the beach!" Steffi replied.

But Steffi's trip to the beach the next day was delayed by scores of calls from reporters. "My poor father was on the phone for five hours with everybody who called the hotel suite," Steffi said. "I just wanted to go to the beach, but he kept handing me the phone, telling me to talk to these people."

At first, it didn't seem that Steffi would really be able to relax after taking the top spot. But there were already signs that Steffi's life was starting to loosen up. Little by little, Mr. Graf was beginning to give her room to grow. Steffi was 18 now, almost an adult, and he could see that she wanted more independence.

Steffi's father began letting Steffi travel with Pavel Slozil instead of him. Her father waited until Steffi would call and say "Papa, I miss you." Then he would board a plane and join her.

A West German reporter, Conny Konzack, had known Steffi since she was in the German juniors, and Conny noticed the change. "Steffi used to have her father around a lot," Conny said. "He would interrupt her at news conferences, and tell her what to say. But that's past. She really knows what she wants."

Shortly before Steffi became Number 1, she bought a home in Delray Beach, Florida, not far from Boca Raton. Steffi practiced at the Gleneagles Country Club. She had just been named the "resident touring professional," which only meant that Steffi practiced on the country club's courts when she was staying in Florida. "I seem to spend most of my time in the United States," Steffi said, "and Gleneagles has tennis courts with all three surfaces—clay, grass and all-weather."

Steffi's life became easier once she had a place she could call home in the United States. It's not easy living out of a hotel room.

Steffi was also beginning to open up more to other women tennis players. When Steffi started on the tour, she was 13 years old and very shy. Some players, though, thought that Steffi was a snob, or that her father had too much control over her. "I'm not sure Steffi's father would let her get close to another player," Martina says. "I think she's a really nice kid, but I'm the one who instigates most of our conversations."

A top woman player approached Steffi's father at the end of 1986. "Steffi never speaks to me," she said. Mr. Graf recalls having told her that "she should be the one to go to Steffi because Steffi is younger, so it is harder for her to go to the older ones. It's not easy for a young player when she comes into the Top 10. Other players don't like that. Now [in 1987], she is Number 1, so there will be some loneliness. It is that way with all champions."

Steffi wasn't forming any close friendships with other women tennis players, though. It was too difficult for her to be close to the people she had to compete against. She did start to get more friendly, though. "I had to get used to everything when I started on the tour," she said. "That's why I was a little more distant with people before, and now I'm more open."

However, one player had grown to like Steffi less. That was Martina. "Martina was nice to me when I was younger," Steffi said. "But relations have gotten a bit cooler since I've gotten so successful. These days Martina is a little scared of me."

Meanwhile, Martina was dismayed by the year she had been having. Her only victory was at Wimbledon. Still, Martina thought that she, not Steffi, should be ranked Number 1, and the U.S. Open would prove who really deserved the title. "I've always said anyone who wins the U.S. Open and Wimbledon in the same year should be Number 1," Martina said. "It doesn't really matter what happens the rest of the year."

Unfortunately for Martina, it *did* matter what happened during the rest of the year. Even if Martina beat Steffi at the Open, she wouldn't be able to regain the top spot. And that made Martina furious.

Steffi had planned to play in the Mahwah, New Jersey, tournament a few weeks before the U.S. Open. She usually played in that tournament because the courts have the same surface as the ones at the U.S. Open, which make it a good warm-up.

One week before Steffi was scheduled to play, however, she underwent emergency root canal surgery in Florida. Before the surgery, her tooth had hurt her so much that she couldn't even serve in practice. Officials in Mahwah moved her starting time back so that she could still compete, but Steffi had developed an infection and she had to skip the tournament altogether. Steffi arrived in New York just in time to play the U.S. Open.

And then to make matters worse, Steffi came down with a fever and flu during the U.S. Open. She often gets sick when she visits New York, but she still loves the city. She enjoys going to all the different restaurants and shopping—especially for new compact discs.

Luckily, Steffi's physical woes didn't have much of an effect on her game. She defeated her third-round opponent, Patricia Tarabini of Argentina, in only 38 minutes. Patricia, though, is a friend of Steffi's and she found it hard competing against Steffi. "Steffi's one of my best friends on the tour," said Patricia. "Sometimes during the first set I found myself laughing, which I had to change." Steffi beat her 6-2, 6-0.

Steffi made it to the final match. So did Martina, and the older player was out for blood. She was not about to sit idly by while a young upstart took over the Number 1 spot. Steffi and Martina played on a Saturday evening in early September. Steffi was still feeling feverish, and constantly wiped the sweat from her brow. She didn't have the energy she usually has. Steffi wasn't hitting her backhand well at first, and then she wasn't hitting her forehand well near the end of the match. She made 31 unforced errors. That means the errors were her fault; they weren't caused by Martina's tricky plays. Martina won 7-6, 6-1.

Steffi and her father were very upset. Martina went over to console Steffi, but Mr. Graf pulled his daughter away. Then he screamed at a photographer to leave them alone.

Sometimes, it's harder to watch someone you love lose than to lose yourself.

Martina insisted that she was truly Number 1, now that she'd won Wimbledon and the U.S. Open. She said that Steffi had won more, but less important, tournaments. "It's close," Martina said. "It depends on if you're going for quantity or quality. Steffi has great quantity. I have great quality."

"The ranking says I'm still Number 1, and she's still Number 2," Steffi replied. "I'm not going to say anything against that."

Steffi went home to play a few tournaments in Europe and spend time with her family. In the fall, the Grafs like to hike in nearby mountains and pick apples. Steffi and her mom usually make apple cake, a traditional German dessert.

Of course, Steffi never strayed too far from the tennis court. She won a tournament in Hamburg, West Germany, only a few weeks after the Open. Her sinuses, though, were starting to bother her. By October, her sinus problem had gotten so bad that she checked into a hospital in Freiburg, West Germany. Her doctor recommended that she have surgery. But Steffi and her father decided against an operation. She took medicine instead, and hoped that the problem would clear up on its own. Steffi took three weeks off to recover.

Steffi needed to win only one more tournament in 1987 to prove that she deserved the Number 1 title—the Virginia Slims Championships in New York in November. The Slims tournament is very competitive; only the 16 best women players in the world are invited to Madison Square Garden for the championships.

Steffi expected to meet Martina in the final game. Gabriela Sabatini, though, eliminated Martina in the quarter-finals. Martina had played nervously and lost by a score of 6-4, 7-5.

"This tournament was a chance for me to prove I was Number 1," Martina said, "and I felt the pressure. Steffi is Number 1. I know I'm the better player, but I didn't prove it this year."

Gabriela advanced to the final match against Steffi. In most women's tournaments, the first player to win two sets wins the match. In the Slims final, though, a player has to win three sets. Gabriela won the first set, and Steffi won the second. After that, Gabriela grew tired and lost the next two sets. Steffi won, 4-6, 6-4, 6-0, 6-4.

When Steffi earned the final point, she broke into a huge smile. It was the first time that she had won the Slims Championship, and she was filled with joy. "This was the biggest win I've ever had," she said.

The Slims tournament was the last competition of the season, and what a season it had been. Steffi had won 11 tournaments, and her match record for the year was 75-2. Her only losses had come against Martina. She had also earned $1,378,128 in one year.

After the Slims final, reporters wanted her to sum up her year. Steffi was creative with her answer. "If I was a cook, this would be the menu describing my year," she said. "The appetizers were Key Biscayne, Boca Raton and Amelia Island, which I won in the spring. The main course was the French Open topped by Berlin and Rome, all of which I won in the summer. Dessert was Hamburg, Zurich and now, New York." Dessert turned out to be Steffi's favorite part of the meal.

"Not enough salt and pepper at Wimbledon and the U.S. Open," Steffi joked. Those were the only tournaments she'd lost.

"Nobody expected it to happen like this," Steffi said. "It's been an amazing year."

7

The Golden Grand Slam

After resting at home in Brühl and enjoying Christmas with her family, Steffi started the new year in joyous fashion. Her parents threw a party for her at a German disco in early January. They invited Steffi's friends from home. Of course, Steffi's parents and her brother, Michael, were also there. Steffi had a great time dancing with her friends and just being a normal teenager. She had many reasons to celebrate.

By the middle of January, Steffi was in Melbourne, Australia, to play in the Australian Open. Australia is a country south of the equator, and it's called the "Land Down Under" because it's located below the equator. Melbourne is on the southeast coast of Australia.

For many years, the Australian Open was played at Melbourne's Kooyong Club, which has 29 grass courts. The Kooyong Club is almost as rich in tennis tradition as Wimbledon, but the club was too small to host a major international tournament. So the Australians decided to build a new stadium called the National Tennis Center. The 1988 Australian Open was the first tournament ever played at the new stadium.

The National Tennis Center was nothing like Kooyong. It was a well-planned stadium, large and modern. The courts had a hard surface instead of grass. Also, the stadium court had a retractable roof over it, so that matches could be played even if it was raining. The weather in Melbourne can go from intense heat to freezing rain in a matter of hours.

Steffi's tennis game going into the tournament was as well planned as the new stadium. Although she had won only one Grand Slam tournament, she was already considered unbeatable. Even Chris Evert, who had won the Australian twice before, didn't stand much of a chance. Chris had defeated Martina in the semifinals to face Steffi in the final.

Dark clouds hung over the stadium court as the two began to play. Steffi won two out of three games before rain began to fall. The game was stopped for 90 minutes while officials closed the roof and waited for the court to dry.

During the delay, Chris watched the Larry Holmes-Mike Tyson boxing match on television. Tyson knocked Holmes out. After the rain delay, Steffi did the same thing to Chris. Steffi won the first set, 6-1 and was ahead, 4-0, in the second when Chris suddenly woke up. "I was thinking of Larry Holmes," said Chris. "That was me on the ground. I said to myself, out of desperation, 'Do something!'"

Chris did do something—she won a string of games and forced a tiebreaker. But Steffi went for the knockout and won the tiebreaker, 7-3. Steffi had just won a second Grand Slam tournament, her first of the new year. She was still only 18 years old.

"It was a good start to the year," Steffi said, "the best I could have had." The win was so convincing that the press was already beginning to whisper about Steffi winning a Grand Slam. All she had to do was go on to win the French Open, Wimbledon and the U.S. Open in the same year. No big deal!

In March, though, Gabriela Sabatini decided to give Steffi a lesson in losing. Steffi was living in her Florida home at the time, and was playing in the Boca Raton tournament. She faced Gaby in the final.

Many people thought that Gabriela was Steffi's greatest threat, but Steffi had beaten her all 11 times they had played. Although Gabriela was almost Steffi's equal in talent, she lacked the West German's physical stamina and mental concentration. However, at this tournament Gaby beat Steffi 2-6, 6-3, 6-1. The Argentinean was thrilled.

And then only a month later, Gaby did it again. This time, the two met in the semifinal game of the Amelia Island tournament in Florida. Gabriela won the first set, and Steffi won the second. Then Steffi pulled ahead 3-0 in the third, but Gaby wouldn't give up. Although she was near exhaustion, she hung in there and evened the score at 3-3. Then Gaby went on to win the set, 7-5.

Steffi was furious. People were beginning to think that she was losing her grip on the Number 1 spot. She had to prove that no woman could play tennis better than she could. She got her chance in the semifinals of the French Open in June. Steffi was the defending champion, and she wasn't about to let Gaby stop a repeat performance. She beat Gaby in two sets, 6-3, 7-6.

Now, it was Steffi's turn to be thrilled. She had silenced the Sabatini threat. But, in a way, she should have been grateful to Gaby. The losses in Florida may have been what Steffi needed to sharpen her game and her desire to win.

In the final match of the French Open, Steffi humiliated her opponent, 17-year-old Natalia Zvereva [*ZVER-ay-vah*] of the Soviet Union. Steffi beat Natalia, 6-0, 6-0, in just 32 minutes!

When the match was over, Steffi went to the grandstand, jumped up to kiss her father, and went to the award ceremony to receive her silver championship cup. Steffi had won so quickly and so easily that in her speech to the crowd, she apologized. She thanked the crowd for cheering her on and then said, "But I am very sorry it was so short." Steffi knew that some people paid a lot of money to watch her play.

Now Steffi was halfway to winning a Grand Slam. She turned 19 years old ten days after the French Open, and she began to acknowledge publicly that she wanted to win the Slam. It would not be easy, though. The Slam was one of the rarest feats in all of sports. Only four players before Steffi had won it. Don Budge won the Slam in 1938, Rod Laver of Australia won it in 1962 and 1969, Maureen Connolly of the U.S. won it in 1953 and Margaret Court of Australia had done so in 1970.

But Steffi couldn't dwell on the Slam. She needed to win Wimbledon if she had any interest in joining this highly exclusive group. Wimbledon would be the toughest leg of the Slam for Steffi. She still didn't have much experience playing on grass and she suspected she would be meeting Martina in the final. Martina is left-handed and usually serves to Steffi's backhand. If Steffi wanted to beat Martina, she had to strengthen her backhand return. That's exactly what she did.

For four months before Wimbledon, Steffi practiced against Markus Schur, a left-handed German player. For hours on end, Markus sent lefty serves flying at Steffi's backhand until she could return the balls with confidence.

But Martina would not be an easy opponent. She had already tied Helen Wills Moody's record by winning the tournament eight times—and now Martina wanted to *break* the record.

And Martina was also still insisting that Steffi wasn't really the Number 1 player. After all, Steffi hadn't won the two most important tournaments in tennis—Wimbledon and the U.S. Open. "I'd rather win Wimbledon than be Number 1," Martina said.

Even though she knew how badly Martina wanted to win, Steffi wasn't frightened. "Martina has won Wimbledon so many times, she is the favorite," Steffi said. "This is her surface. But last year, I was content just to reach the final. This time, I would like to win."

Steffi and Martina both made it to the final, as expected. Surprisingly, Chris Evert predicted that her friend Martina would lose. "Martina's body language looks confident," Chris said before the Wimbledon final, "but I can tell she isn't."

Martina and Chris had played one another in the semifinals. On the fourth match point, Chris hit a ball and she thought it landed on the line. Martina disagreed, and asked the linesman whether the ball was in or out. He thought about it for a moment, and finally declared the ball out. Because of his call, Martina won the point and the match. Chris was fuming.

When Martina and Steffi played their match, Chris's prediction came true. Steffi beat Martina 5-7, 6-2, 6-1. "I got blown out," Martina said. After Steffi played her last point, she raised both arms, fists clenched, in a victory stance. Then, she tossed her racket into the box seats with joy. Steffi had won her first Wimbledon, and she was the first German woman in 57 years to win the tournament.

Helmut Kohl, the chancellor of West Germany, was so impressed that he sent Steffi a note. "You have come a giant step closer to a Grand Slam with your new success," he wrote. "Along with other tennis fans, I fervently hope that you succeed at achieving this goal."

The victory boosted Steffi's confidence—and proved to Martina that Steffi truly deserved to be ranked first. Martina turned out to be a gracious loser. "This is how it should happen," Martina said. "I lost to a better player on the final day. This is the end of a chapter, passing the torch, if you want to call it that." Martina gave Steffi a good-luck silver tennis racket charm, a gift from boxer Sugar Ray Leonard that Martina had worn at Wimbledon the year before.

The next evening, a dinner was held for the Wimbledon champions. Don Budge was there celebrating the 50th anniversary of his Slam. He congratulated Steffi and said to her, "When, not if, but *when* you win the U.S. Open for your Grand Slam, I hope they'll let me present the trophy to you."

Don Budge wasn't the only person who had so much faith in Steffi. Tennis fans and the tennis press began to wonder if anyone could challenge Steffi. She was so much better than the other players that no one could catch up with her.

The other women tennis players were so sure she would win the U.S. Open, the last leg of the Slam, that they joked that Steffi would lose only if she broke a leg. Still, they wanted desperately to stop her. A few players got together and decided to play their very best tennis against Steffi in hopes of eliminating her from the Open. "Martina and Pam Shriver and I all talked about it," said Chris Evert. "We'll try to stop her. All the girls will be extra conscientious about Graf."

Despite the women's efforts, it was Steffi's German shepherd, Max, who came the closest to stopping her. A month before the Open, Steffi was at home in Germany when Max started fighting with the neighbor's cocker spaniel. When Steffi tried to break the fight up, Max bit her right hand, hard. Steffi had to go to the doctor and have a cast put on the hand. Fortunately, her hand recovered in time for the Open.

Her other obstacle was herself. There was so much pressure on her to win the Slam. The Open was being televised in 50 countries, and all of her matches were being broadcast live in West Germany, no matter the hour. "More than anything, winning the Grand Slam is a battle within yourself," said Margaret Court, who won the Slam in 1970. "It really gets down to how you handle pressure more than how you handle anybody else. Steffi has to forget about the press and the television and not read and listen to what people say about her. You don't want to let the pressure build within yourself."

Steffi responds well to pressure. She ignores what other people are saying and concentrates on the task at hand. When a reporter from *The New York Times* asked her about the Slam, she replied, "It's the U.S. Open I'm trying to win. Ask me about the Grand Slam if I do it."

When the tournament began, it seemed as though Steffi was fated to win it. The "Stop Graf" movement by the other players failed. Zina Garrison upset Martina in the quarter-finals, so Martina couldn't stop Steffi. Then, Chris came down with a stomach flu and had to withdraw from her semifinal match against the West German.

Steffi didn't exactly get off easy, though. She had to face one of her toughest opponents in the final—Gabriela Sabatini. Steffi started the match nervously, as if she could feel all the pressure on her. But she gradually regained her confidence. The more confident she became, the more tired Gaby seemed. As 21,000 fans watched at the National Tennis Center, Steffi beat her 6-3, 3-6, 6-1. Steffi had won the Grand Slam!

She rushed over to where Pavel, her mom, dad and brother were sitting and hugged them all. The tournament officials raised the flags of the Grand Slam countries—Australia, France, Great Britain and the United States—in honor of her feat. And Gordon Jorgensen, president of the U.S. Tennis Association, presented Steffi with a Grand Slam bracelet. The bracelet was gold and had four diamonds on it, one for each Grand Slam tournament.

Don Budge was there, too, just as he had promised. When he congratulated her, he said he thought that she would win several more Grand Slams during her career. After all, Steffi was only 19 and probably not at the peak of her tennis game yet.

Steffi had accomplished an amazing feat. Winning the Slam didn't seem all that exciting, though. The fans weren't cheering wildly because they had expected her to win all along. And Steffi didn't jump up for joy. In a way, she was glad the tournament was over. "It's a relief," she said. "Now I've done it. There's no more pressure. Now, there's nothing else that people can tell me I have to do."

Steffi suffered from the curse of the straight-A student. Everybody expected her to do well, so they weren't surprised when she did. The only way Steffi could turn a head in 1988 was by losing.

In a way, she had won the Slam too early. She was only 19 years old and tennis fans were just getting used to the idea of her being Number 1. In 1987, she only won one Grand Slam event, then the next year she turned around and won all four!

The year wasn't over yet. The evening Steffi won the Open, she went back to Germany and rested for three days before leaving for Seoul, South Korea, and the Summer Olympics.

For some time, Steffi's business agents had been trying

to decide what they would call a combination of a Grand Slam and an Olympic gold medal in case Steffi won both. Finally, they came up with it: the Golden Grand Slam. Now, all Steffi had to do was win.

When she arrived in Seoul, she was tired. The stress of the Slam had taken its toll. To make matters worse, she was mobbed by photographers and journalists the moment she stepped off the plane at the Seoul airport. The scene became so chaotic that Steffi burst into tears.

"When I came to Seoul, I was really tired," she said. "I wanted some time to be away. It took three or four days to get used to everything. The Olympics are a little different than other tournaments."

At most tennis tournaments, the players stay in luxury hotels, and they're treated like stars. At the Olympics, however, the tennis players stay at the Olympic Village with all the other athletes. The Village is similar to a college dorm—no frills. In professional tennis, players can win enormous sums of money. In the Olympics, athletes compete only for individual honor and the honor of their country.

Had Steffi not been so tired, she would have enjoyed the village more. She was especially fond of the Olympics because she had won the 1984 demonstration event as a 15-year-old. She also liked meeting outstanding athletes from other sports. When she had free time during the Olympics, Steffi rode her bike to watch other events. She even went to see a boxing match because a friend of hers from the Netherlands was competing.

But the longer Steffi stayed in Seoul, the more enthusiastic she got. She practiced harder and played harder. In the final, she faced Gabriela Sabatini and beat her 6-3, 6-3.

Steffi had done it. She won a gold medal for West Germany, and became the first tennis player ever to win a Golden Grand Slam!

Now it was over. She had a moment to relax and think how successful she had been. "Winning the Grand Slam and then the gold medal—that's amazing," she said. "I think it is something not many people after me will achieve."

8

Growing Up

As the 1989 season began, Steffi was again besieged by the press. This time, however, reporters were interested in what she was doing off the court. Steffi had her first boyfriend.

Alexander Mronz [*mah-RONZ*] was a 24-year-old tennis player from Cologne, West Germany. At the time he started dating Steffi, Alex was ranked 278th in the world. He rose more than 100 spots in the rankings over the course of nine months. He also won his first professional tournament ever, on Martinique, an island in the West Indies. Obviously, Steffi taught him a thing or two about tennis.

The press first learned about Steffi and Alexander when

she played in the Australian Open. He was there also, and they went out a couple of times in Melbourne. Later, he visited Steffi at her home in Florida. Many people expected that Steffi's father would be jealous of any boyfriend she had. But Mr. Graf was happy for her.

"This is good for Steffi, good for all of us," said Steffi's father. "It is time for the break. We knew it would be hard on the first boyfriend. But I think Steffi can make good judgments. Alexander is a tennis player. He knows tennis comes Number 1 with Steffi. I think this is a good arrangement. At the end of the day, if she says to him, 'It is nine o'clock now, I have to go to bed,' he says, 'Goodnight,' and lets her go. I think everything is okay."

The German press went crazy. For years, they had been reporting gossip about Boris Becker. Now, finally, there was something to say about Steffi. *Bild*, a West German magazine, ran an article on Steffi and Alex. The headline said, "Steffi: Will an Engagement Come Within the Year?"

"If they ask me about this subject, I have an answer for them," Steffi told Curry Kirkpatrick of *Sports Illustrated*. "I'm going to say, 'Haven't you heard? It's all set. I'm already picking out a wedding dress.'"

She was only joking, but that is the best way to deal with the exaggerations in the press. When reporters weren't asking about Alexander, they were asking about a second Grand Slam. Steffi was playing so well that there was a good chance she'd become the first person ever to win back-to-back Slams. "I don't want to hear that question," she replied, when asked about a second Slam. "I've already said it's very difficult. It's not impossible, but it's unlikely."

She didn't want people to think she was perfect. It was too much responsibility for a 19-year-old. "With the competition now, you can always lose," she told Bruce Newman of *Sports Illustrated.* "To be perfect for a year is not possible. Don't ask that of me, please."

The Grand Slam of 1988 had put enough pressure on Steffi. Her health wasn't good after the time she spent in Seoul. She came down with a cold that turned into bronchitis by November. After the Virginia Slims tournament in New York, where she lost to Pam Shriver, Steffi stayed in bed for three weeks in Florida. She recovered in time to ski in Austria for a week, and then went home to Germany for Christmas. But she had learned her lesson. She needed time to rest and relax.

Even though she didn't want to talk about a second Grand Slam, she started the year with a repeat performance. With the temperature at 100 degrees in Melbourne, Steffi defeated Helena Sukova, 6-4, 6-4, to win the Australian Open. She didn't lose a set in the whole tournament.

Soon enough, though, Steffi would put an end to talk of a second Grand Slam. A few weeks before her twentieth birthday, Steffi arrived in Paris to play the French Open. Her father was at home in Brühl with the flu, and he missed the first 12 days of the tournament. Steffi was worried about him. She wasn't feeling too well herself.

On the Tuesday before the Saturday final, she ate a piece of pizza that didn't agree with her. She had to play both her semifinal and final matches between bouts of vomiting. She lost seven pounds and most of her energy.

Martina and Chris both decided to skip the French Open. Martina wanted more time to practice on grass to prepare for Wimbledon. And Chris needed time out from the tour's pressure. Chris was also thinking about retiring, and wanted to relax and think about it.

Everyone expected that Steffi would walk all over the remaining field. But Steffi's opposition was a group of young and very eager players who wanted to prove themselves against the champ. Steffi made it much further than her boyfriend Alex, though. He lost in the first round of the tournament.

Steffi faced Monica Seles, a 15-year-old from Yugoslavia, in the semifinal. Seles is considered one of the best young players on the tour. She has powerful strokes and intelligent strategy, as well as a strong will to win. And she made Steffi work for a win. Monica took Steffi to three sets before Steffi won, 6-3, 3-6, 6-3.

All Monica did, though, was soften Steffi up for Aranxta Sanchez Vicario in the final. Steffi's father showed up for the final, but he still wasn't feeling well. He left to fly back home after the first set.

Aranxta, who lives in Barcelona, Spain, was 17 years old at the time. She was easily as fit as Steffi, and she hit crosscourt forehands that kept Steffi running. Their match lasted for three hours. Aranxta won the first set, 7-6, and then Steffi won the next set, 6-3. By the third set, Steffi was feeling so terrible that she had to leave the court for a few minutes. When she returned, she lost 16 of the next 19 points, and Aranxta won the match.

Aranxta had become the youngest woman ever to win the French Open, and the first Spanish woman ever to win a Grand Slam event. She was so excited that she burst into tears and rushed into Steffi's arms. Steffi embraced her warmly, as though she was almost relieved that somebody had finally beaten her. Now there wouldn't be so much pressure on her to win.

"Aranxta really played a great match," Steffi said. "She's one of the people who just enjoys tennis. She's a great person and I feel so good for her."

Because of the loss, Steffi gained a new appreciation for her previous victories. "When you lose a couple of times, it makes you realize how difficult it is to win. There were times last year when I just didn't know how much I was winning and how tough it was."

That's not to say that Steffi liked losing. She is a champion, and champions don't get to the top spot by enjoying a loss. "It took me three days to get over the Paris loss," Steffi said. "It was certainly not easy." Steffi planned to avenge the French Open loss by winning at Wimbledon.

Steffi's boyfriend, Alex, couldn't come to London for the Wimbledon tournament. He was in West Germany having knee surgery. "I'm more worried about my father," she said. Her father had been flying back and forth to West Germany because he was suffering from stomach pains. Luckily, he turned out to be fine.

As for Alex, he and Steffi broke up before the U.S. Open began in September. Steffi was reportedly not happy that Alex had been so public about their relationship.

Neither Steffi's father nor Alex, though, affected her performance at Wimbledon. As expected, Steffi faced Martina in the final. And Steffi won, 6-2, 6-7, 6-1. In an unusual display of emotion, Steffi burst into tears of joy as soon as she had won.

"When I was ahead three games to one in the third set, I felt like the match was all over," Steffi said. "I had that winning feeling so much that I had to tell myself: 'C'mon, you still have to play some tennis.' But I was so loose. Everything was coming so easy. I was really enjoying myself."

Martina was awed by what she saw. "Steffi is the fastest player on the circuit," she said. "I don't think our age difference has anything to do with my loss. She's a sprinter. She's a track-and-field athlete."

That was true. Erco Pruell, Steffi's fitness trainer in West Germany, said that Steffi could run 800 meters in two minutes, five seconds—a competitive time for most college racers. "Her mixture of speed and endurance is so good it's not normal," Erco said. "Steffi can play four hours of tennis, do an hour of conditioning with me and then do 100-meter sprint intervals."

Steffi wasn't the only victorious West German at Wimbledon. Her friend Boris Becker won the men's singles. He defeated Stefan Edberg 6-0, 7-6, 6-4. It was the first time since 1934 that the women's and men's winners both came from the same European country.

Steffi was thrilled for Boris, and Boris was thrilled for Steffi. They had joined one another for dinner one evening during the tournament, and wished one another good luck. "I know Steffi almost better than anybody," Boris said. "We more or less went through the same tournaments when we were young. So it is a fairy tale that we should both win Wimbledon in the same year."

Steffi and Boris shared victories again in September, this time in New York. Their championships, though, were not the big news of the 1989 U.S. Open. That honor went to

Chris Evert who had just made a big decision.

Before the Open began, Chris announced that this would be her last tournament ever. She was 34 years old, married to Alpine skier Andy Mill and she wanted to start a family. Chris had achieved all of her goals in tennis, and now it was time to try something else. Chris made it through a tough match against Monica Seles in the early rounds and faced Zina Garrison in the quarterfinals. Zina didn't want to be the "villain" who eliminated Chris, but Zina didn't want to lose either. She beat Chris, 7-6, 6-2. Then Zina ran to Chris and put her arm around her, to show her respect.

After Chris was eliminated, the press focused its attention again on Steffi, who struggled through a semifinal game against Gabriela. The temperature on the court that day rose as high as 120 degrees. Steffi was getting too hot, and she wasn't drinking enough water. The muscles in her legs began to cramp and her face was contorted with pain during the last set. Her legs hurt so much that she couldn't sit down during the changeover breaks.

Steffi gathered all of her strength and went on to beat Gaby 3-6, 6-4, 6-2. As soon as the match was finished, Steffi rushed off the court to the see a doctor. She was treated with ice and massage and she drank a lot of water to combat her dehydration.

Luckily, Steffi's legs had fully recovered in time to play the final against Martina the next day. Martina didn't feel very lucky, however. Steffi beat her 3-6, 7-5, 6-1. When the match was finished both women threw their rackets into the air—Steffi because she was so happy, Martina because she was so mad. Martina had played brilliantly in the beginning of the match, but then lost her momentum in the second set. The 1989 season was nearing an end, and Martina hadn't won a single Grand Slam tournament.

Pavel Slozil and Steffi's dad were surprised that Steffi had won the Open. They knew how good she was, but they also knew how much she had suffered in the semifinal. "I hoped she had a chance, but I didn't believe she could win," Steffi's dad said. "But that is Steffi. If she's close to losing, she can bring herself to the front." So could Boris. He beat Ivan Lendl in the final, 7-6, 1-6, 6-3, 7-6. The "Deutschland Duo" had done it again. (Deutschland [*DOYCH-lant*] is the German word for Germany.)

Steffi still wanted to win the Virginia Slims Championships. She had lost in the semifinals of the tournament the year before, and she wanted to avenge the loss. "I was very disappointed that I could not win there last year," she said. "It would have been a perfect ending to an incredible year for me, but it just didn't happen that way. This year, I hope it will be a different story."

When Steffi arrived in New York in November for the tournament, though, she was distracted. Dramatic changes were taking place at home in Germany. Since 1949, Germany has been divided; on the west side is West Germany, on the east is East Germany.

East Germany is a communist country, with tight control over its citizens. Ever since the early 1950s, East Germans have not been allowed to travel freely out of their country.

The West Germans, meanwhile, enjoy much greater freedom. But in the fall of 1989, that began to change. The East German government leadership changed, and declared that people would be allowed to travel freely. East Germans could go to West Germany to visit friends and relatives anytime they wanted to.

During November, when Steffi was in New York, East and West Germans celebrated by using hammers and ice picks to chip away at the wall in the city of Berlin that had divided them. East Germans poured by the hundreds of thousands into West Berlin, which soon turned into a huge and joyous party. Steffi wanted to be a part of it. For three days in the beginning of November, Steffi had been trying to reach a friend in West Berlin. Each time, she reached only his answering machine. "Sorry I'm not here," the machine said. "I'm out partying and I won't be home for a while."

Steffi seemed envious. "I would love to have been there," she said, "just to have been part of the moment."

Steffi had never been to East Germany. She said that more than a third of her fan mail in Germany came from East Germans, most of whom had never been able to see her play in person.

She recalled once having received a letter from a young East German girl who wanted to compete as a tennis player in West Germany. "She asked me if I could help her in any way," Steffi said. "But I couldn't."

Steffi wanted to be home celebrating the changes in Germany. But despite the distraction, she was able to concentrate on tennis. She defeated Gaby, the defending Slims champion, in the semifinals. Then, in a repeat of the U.S.

Open, she defeated Martina in a four-set final. The score was 6-4, 7-5, 2-6, 6-2.

Steffi felt bad, in a way, for Martina. Martina had played her hardest, but still lost. After the match, Steffi went over to Martina and apologized to her for the defeat. "Sorry about that," Steffi said.

"I told her, 'Don't be sorry. Enjoy it. You deserve it.'" said Martina. "I think Steffi gets so wrapped up in her tennis. But when she stops and thinks, she can be gracious. She's basically a very good human being with a good heart."

In truth, Martina wasn't all that upset about her loss. She was practically singing in the shower later because she found the tough match so inspiring. "When I was in the shower I said to myself, 'Why am I smiling? I lost,'" Martina said. "But if it wasn't for Steffi, I wouldn't still be playing. She's my curse as well as my blessing."

Steffi was happy, too. Even though she hadn't won another Grand Slam, she still had a remarkable year. "This year, I lost only two matches [to Gaby and to Aranxta] and I was too sick to do anything when I lost to Aranxta at the French," Steffi said. "This was an unbelievable year."

9

Alone at the Top

Steffi's dad agreed that Steffi's year had been good. But he thinks the best is yet to come. "Steffi is really developing her game," he said. "She will do it more and more on a higher level." Pavel Slozil thought that Steffi would reach her peak in two or three more years.

Steffi probably will improve her game. She's already done whatever was necessary to improve. At the same time, she pushes other players to improve their games. "Steffi has caused the others to try to catch up to her level," says Chris Evert. As Steffi becomes better and better, will there be anyone who will be able to challenge her? It is a question that is asked over and over in the tennis press.

Her greatest challenge now is Martina. Martina is as competitive and talented as Steffi. She also has a brilliant understanding of the game. But Martina is 12 years older than the reigning champion, and will probably retire in a couple of years. If Martina and Steffi had been the same age, they might have had an even greater rivalry than Martina and Chris.

The press has tried to tout Gabriela Sabatini as the player most likely to knock Steffi off her throne. Gaby causes problems for Steffi because she uses a variety of spins on her shots. The shots dip as they come across the net, and it's hard to predict where they'll land—and at what angle they'll bounce.

Gaby is one of the only players who routinely forces Steffi to play three sets. "She's tested Steffi more than any of the top players," says Chris. In 1988, she handed Steffi two of her three defeats, and in 1989, one of two losses.

But unless Gaby makes dramatic changes, she seems an unlikely Number 1. She tends to tire easily and lose her concentration during matches. She hired a new coach, Angel Gimenez, in 1987. Angel started Gaby running for about an hour a day, and her stamina has increased. But neither her stamina nor her concentration come close to Steffi's. "Gaby still has a tendency to go through mood swings on the court," says Donald Dell, Gaby's business agent. "You watch Steffi and she has no mood swings. She wants to kill you on every point."

Most likely, the threat to Steffi's Number 1 ranking will come from the younger ranks of women's tennis: Aranxta Sanchez Vicario, Monica Seles and Jennifer Capriati.

Aranxta was the player who deprived Steffi of a second Grand Slam by defeating her in the French Open. Before that, Aranxta had won only two professional tournaments. By the end of 1989, she was already ranked Number 4 in the world.

Aranxta has limitless energy, good footwork and a deadly drop shot. She also has a go-for-it mentality. She will run down anything if it means she'll win a point. "Aranxta is sweet," says her coach, Juan Nuñez. "But on the court she is a lion."

But Aranxta will need to become more versatile if she has any hopes of a Number 1 ranking. She is a threat to Steffi on clay, the surface on which she learned to play, but she has trouble on grass. Aranxta took three months off from competition at the beginning of 1990 to work on improving her game.

Monica Seles is a more versatile player, and many people think she will move into the Number 2 spot in a matter of years. Monica is from Novi Sad, Yugoslavia. In 1989, she and her family moved to Florida so that she could spend more time with her coach, Nick Bolletieri. Nick also coached Andre Agassi when he was younger.

Monica, at 16, is still young, and she has the eagerness of youth. She isn't scared by the older, more established players. At the French Open in 1989, she was one of a few players to take Steffi to three sets. Monica regularly made it to the later rounds of tournaments. She qualified for the Virginia Slims Championships in New York, which feature the sport's top 16 players. By the end of the year, Monica was ranked seventh in the world.

Monica has an unusual style, hitting both her backhand and forehand with two hands. But she gets tremendous power out of her strokes. She hits them so hard that she grunts loudly with every hit, as if every point might be her last. The grunts have drawn quite a bit of attention. "Monica used to sound like a Christmas goose being strangled to death," says tennis observer Ted Tinling. "But she's gotten much better."

It's still too early in Monica's career to say whether she can become Number 1. The same is true of Jennifer Capriati, a 14-year-old from Florida. Jennifer turned pro in the spring of 1990, but before that she had won the juniors singles championships at the French Open and the U.S. Open.

The U.S. juniors coaches think that Jennifer's tennis game is advanced well beyond her years. She is a natural athlete, with good footwork and timing. Like Aranxta, she is a sweet girl off the court—and a killer on it.

Jennifer was first coached by Jimmy Evert, Chris's dad. Jennifer adores Chris, and the admiration has been returned. "Jennifer could be in the Top 10 soon," says Chris.

Any one of these women could pose a threat to Steffi in the future. For now, though, Steffi is sitting alone at the top. No one, not even Steffi, knows how long she will continue to play tennis. If she isn't challenged by her opponents in the future, she may become bored. She has already said that she doubts she'll play beyond her 20s.

Like Chris, she may decide to focus on life outside of tennis. Steffi already has some dreams about what she'll do after retirement. "One year I want to work with animals, the next year I want to build a hotel. I want to have kids, that's for sure," Steffi said in 1988. "The reason I'll stop playing is because I will want to get away from it. I'm a perfectionist, always trying to do my best."

Steffi will stay with the game for now. "There is something special inside her. She needs tennis," says Pavel Slozil. "And she's doing it for herself."

Steffi may need tennis, but women's tennis also needs Steffi. "I like Steffi's sporting attitude, shyness and family image," said Margaret Court, who won the Grand Slam in 1970. "She is good for the game. We need young people like her at the top so that the younger players can look up to them."

The young players certainly do look up to Steffi. Someday, one of them will even replace her as Number 1. But no one will be able to replace Steffi Graf as a person. She has already secured her place in the tennis history books, by winning the first Golden Grand Slam ever, and by raising the women's game to a new level. Tennis can ask for no more.

TENNIS COURT

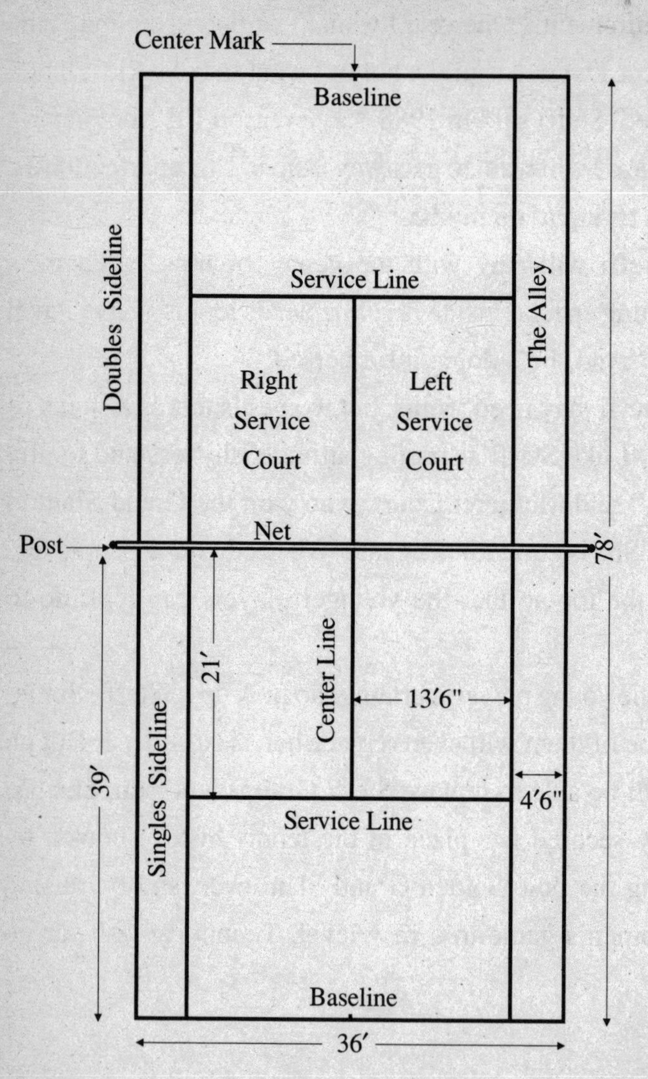

Tennis Terms

Ace:	A serve that is not touched by the receiver and which scores a point for the server.
Backhand:	A stroke made with the arm across the body and the back of the hand turned in the same direction the hitter wants the ball to go.
Baseline:	The boundary that marks the end of the court.
Double-fault:	Failing to place either of two serves in play.
Doubles:	A match between two teams, each team consisting of two players.
Error:	Failure to return the ball legally.

Forehand:	A stroke made with the palm of the hand turned in the direction the hitter wants the ball to go.
Game point:	The point that will win a game if the player who is ahead in the score wins it.
Groundstroke:	Hitting the ball after it has bounced, usually from the area of the baseline.
Match:	A contest between two players (in singles) or four players (in doubles) that is usually the best of three sets.
Match point:	A point that will end the match if the player who is leading wins it.
Serve:	Putting the ball into play, usually with an overhand motion.

Serve-and-volley:	A style of play that involves rushing toward the net immediately after the serve, in order to return the ball before it bounces.
Service break:	When one player wins a game while the other is serving.
Singles:	A match between two players.
Tiebreaker:	A special game that is played when a set is tied at six games apiece. The first player to gain seven points wins, but it must be by two points.
Two-handed backhand:	A backhand stroke with two hands on the grip.
Volley:	Hitting the ball before it bounces.

Highlights of Steffi's Career

1982
Won the German 18-and-under junior championship, and became a professional tennis player.

1984
Olympic tennis champion (tennis was only a demonstration sport in 1984).

1986
Won her first professional tournament, the Family Circle Magazine Cup at Hilton Head, South Carolina.

1987
Won her first Grand Slam tournament, the French Open and became the Number 1 woman tennis player in the world.

1988
Won the Grand Slam (the Australian, French and U.S. Opens and Wimbledon) as well as an Olympic gold medal in Seoul, South Korea.

1989
Australian Open, U.S. Open, Wimbledon Champion.

1990
Australian Open Champion.

NAME:	Stephanie Maria Graf
BIRTHDATE:	June 14, 1969
BIRTHPLACE:	Brühl, West Germany
HOMES:	Brühl, West Germany and Delray Beach, Florida

Steffi's Favorite Things

FAVORITE FOOD:	Apple Pancakes
SPORTS TO WATCH:	Basketball, Soccer
SPORTS TO PLAY:	Basketball, Track
ATHLETES:	Carl Lewis, John McEnroe
MOVIE:	*When Harry Met Sally...*
ACTRESS:	Daryl Hannah
ACTOR:	Willem Dafoe
TELEVISION SHOW:	"Perfect Strangers"
BAND:	Simply Red

More of Steffi's Favorite Things

COLOR:	Black
CAR:	Opel
BOOK:	*The Unbearable Lightness of Being* by Milan Kundera
HOBBIES:	Photography, fashion and visiting museums
FAVORITE ARTICLE OF CLOTHING:	Jeans
THE PLACE SHE WOULD MOST LIKE TO VISIT:	South Africa

GRAND SLAM TOURNAMENT WINNERS
Australian Open Winners (1980-1990)

1980:	Hana Mandlikova
1981:	Martina Navratilova
1982:	Chris Evert
1983:	Martina Navratilova
1984:	Chris Evert
1985:	Martina Navratilova
1986:	Not held; permanently moved from December to January
1987:	Hana Mandlikova
1988:	Steffi Graf
1989:	Steffi Graf
1990:	Steffi Graf

French Open Winners (1979-1989)

1979:	Chris Evert
1980:	Chris Evert
1981:	Hana Mandlikova
1982:	Martina Navratilova
1983:	Chris Evert
1984:	Martina Navratilova
1985:	Chris Evert
1986:	Chris Evert
1987:	Steffi Graf
1988:	Steffi Graf
1989:	Aranxta Sanchez Vicario

Wimbledon Winners (1979-1989)

1979:	Martina Navratilova
1980:	Evonne Goolagong
1981:	Chris Evert
1982:	Martina Navratilova
1983:	Martina Navratilova
1984:	Martina Navratilova
1985:	Martina Navratilova
1986:	Martina Navratilova
1987:	Martina Navratilova
1988:	Steffi Graf
1989:	Steffi Graf

U.S. Open Winners (1979-1989)

1979:	Tracy Austin
1980:	Chris Evert
1981:	Tracy Austin
1982:	Chris Evert
1983:	Martina Navratilova
1984:	Martina Navratilova
1985:	Hana Mandlikova
1986:	Martina Navratilova
1987:	Martina Navratilova
1988:	Steffi Graf
1989:	Steffi Graf

About the Author

Laura Hilgers

Ms. Hilgers is a writer, reporter and editor for *Sports Illustrated For Kids* magazine. She lives in Brooklyn Heights, New York, with her husband, *Sports Illustrated* staff writer Austin Murphy.